THE COMPUTER AND
TELECOMMUNICATIONS HANDBOOK

By the same author

Modular Programming
Computer Programming Management
Basic PL/1
Computer Programming Made Simple
Dictionary of Data Processing
BASIC for Micros

The Computer and Telecommunications Handbook

Jeff Maynard

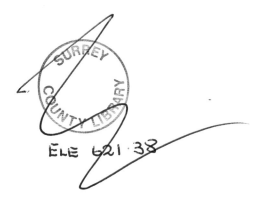

GRANADA
London Toronto Sydney New York

Granada Technical Books
Granada Publishing Ltd
8 Grafton Street, London W1X 3LA

First published in Great Britain by
Granada Publishing 1984

British Library Cataloguing in Publication Data
Maynard, Jeff
    The computer and telecommunications handbook.
    1. Telecommunication—Handbooks, manual, etc.
    I. Title
    621.38′0212   TK5101
    ISBN 0-246-12253-6

Printed and bound in Great Britain by
Mackays of Chatham, Kent

For Helen and RJP

Contents

Preface

This is the sort of book I wish someone else had written at least ten years ago. For, if they had, I would have spent far less time researching for these odd items of reference information which are always necessary for project completion.

Indeed, it was the memories of these searches that prompted me to think about compiling this work. How I searched for such simple but difficult to find items as

- the ASCII code for End of Text,
- the symbol for an FET,
- which country uses the telex answerback HX, and
- how to calculate power loss

only reinforced the view that a single source of reference would be a great help to others in the computing and telecommunications fields.

But what to include in such a book? Would my needs be the same as those of other people? In the latter case, I think the answer is 'substantially, yes', and so I have compiled a collection of information useful to the computer and the telecommunication practitioner.

This is not really a book for browsing, although I am sure many readers will so do, but is essentially a reference work. The programmer, the system designer, the business analyst, the maintenance engineer, the network designer, the student, and the many, many other people involved today in the fields associated with information technology will find this invaluable at their right hand.

Such a work can never be exhaustive, but the bulk of what you will need, but can never find, is here. I hope the time you can save with it will be profitably spent elsewhere.

J. MAYNARD
Cheshire

Acknowledgements

The author would like to thank the Telecommunications Users' Association (TUA) for the support they have pledged to this handbook. The TUA, (to be found at: 34, Grand Avenue, London N10 3BP; tel 01-883 7229), is an independent consumer body whose aims are to ensure that the U.K. telecommunications network serves the users as effectively as possible, making full use of modern technology, and to provide expert advice and representation for its members.

1 Character Codes

ASCII
AMERICAN NATIONAL STANDARD
CODE FOR INFORMATION INTERCHANGE

b_4 b_3 b_2 b_1	COLUMN ROW	0	1	2	3	4	5	6	7
0 0 0 0	0	NUL	DLE	SP	0	@	P		p
0 0 0 1	1	SOH	DC1	!	1	A	Q	a	q
0 0 1 0	2	STX	DC2	"	2	B	R	b	r
0 0 1 1	3	ETX	DC3	#	3	C	S	c	s
0 1 0 0	4	EOT	DC4	$	4	D	T	d	t
0 1 0 1	5	ENQ	NAK	%	5	E	U	e	u
0 1 1 0	6	ACK	SYN	&	6	F	V	f	v
0 1 1 1	7	BEL	ETB	'	7	G	W	g	w
1 0 0 0	8	BS	CAN	(	8	H	X	h	x
1 0 0 1	9	HT	EM	)	9	I	Y	i	y
1 0 1 0	10	LF	SUB	*	:	J	Z	j	z
1 0 1 1	11	VT	ESC	+	;	K	[	k	{
1 1 0 0	12	FF	FS	,	<	L	\	l	|
1 1 0 1	13	CR	GS	–	=	M	]	m	}
1 1 1 0	14	SO	RS	.	>	N	ˆ	n	~
1 1 1 1	15	SI	US	/	?	O	_	o	DEL

(Column header bits: $b_7 b_6 b_5$ = 000, 001, 010, 011, 100, 101, 110, 111 for columns 0–7)

CHARACTER REPRESENTATION AND CODE IDENTIFICATION

The standard 7-bit character representation, with b_7 the high-order bit and b_1 the low-order bit, is shown below:

Example: The bit representation for the character 'K,' positioned in column 4, row 11, is

b_7	b_6	b_5	b_4	b_3	b_2	b_1
1	0	0	1	0	1	1

The code table for the character 'K' may also be represented by the notation 'column 4, row 11' or alternatively as '4/11.' The decimal equivalent of the binary number formed by bits b_7, b_6, and b_5, collectively, forms the column number, and the decimal equivalent of the binary number formed by bits $b_4, b_3, b_2,$ and b_1, collectively, forms the row number.

Control Characters

Col/ Row	Mnemonic and Meaning[1]		Col/ Row	Mnemonic and Meaning[1]	
0/0	NUL	Null	1/0	DLE	Data Link Escape (CC)
0/1	SOH	Start of Heading (CC)	1/1	DC1	Device Control 1
0/2	STX	Start of Text (CC)	1/2	DC2	Device Control 2
0/3	ETX	End of Text (CC)	1/3	DC3	Device Control 3
0/4	EOT	End of Transmission (CC)	1/4	DC4	Device Control 4
0/5	ENQ	Enquiry (CC)	1/5	NAK	Negative Acknowledge (CC)
0/6	ACK	Acknowledge (CC)	1/6	SYN	Synchronous Idle (CC)
0/7	BEL	Bell	1/7	ETB	End of Transmission Block (CC)
0/8	BS	Backspace (FE)	1/8	CAN	Cancel
0/9	HT	Horizontal Tabulation (FE)	1/9	EM	End of Medium
0/10	LF	Line Feed (FE)	1/10	SUB	Substitute
0/11	VT	Vertical Tabulation (FE)	1/11	ESC	Escape
0/12	FF	Form Feed (FE)	1/12	FS	File Separator (IS)
0/13	CR	Carriage Return (FE)	1/13	GS	Group Separator (IS)
0/14	SO	Shift Out	1/14	RS	Record Separator (IS)
0/15	SI	Shift In	1/15	US	Unit Separator (IS)
			7/15	DEL	Delete

[1] (CC) Communication Control; (FE) Format Effector; (IS) Information Separator.

Graphic Characters

Column/Row	Symbol	Name
2/0	SP	Space (Normally Nonprinting)
2/1	!	Exclamation Point
2/2	"	Quotation Marks (Diaeresis)
2/3	#	Number Sign
2/4	$	Dollar Sign
2/5	%	Percent Sign
2/6	&	Ampersand
2/7	'	Apostrophe (Closing Single Quotation Mark; Acute Accent)
2/8	(	Opening Parenthesis
2/9	)	Closing Parenthesis
2/10	*	Asterisk
2/11	+	Plus
2/12	,	Comma (Cedilla)
2/13	–	Hyphen (Minus)
2/14	.	Period (Decimal Point)
2/15	/	Slant
3/0 to 3/9	0 . . . 9	Digits 0 through 9
3/10	:	Colon
3/11	;	Semicolon
3/12	<	Less Than
3/13	=	Equals
3/14	>	Greater Than

Column/Row	Symbol	Name
3/15	?	Question Mark
4/0	@	Commercial At
4/1 to 5/10	A . . . Z	Upper case Latin letters A through Z
5/11	[	Opening Bracket
5/12	\	Reverse Slant
5/13	]	Closing Bracket
5/14	^	Circumflex
5/15	—	Underline
6/0	`	Opening Single Quotation Mark (Grave Accent)
6/1 to 7/10	a . . . z	Lower case Latin letters a through z
7/11	{	Opening Brace
7/12	|	Vertical Line
7/13	}	Closing Brace
7/14	~	Tilde

ASCII
(OCTAL AND HEXADECIMAL)

ASCII CODE SET

ASCII CODES					
GRAPHIC	OCTAL	HEX			
NUL	000	00	CAN	030	18
SOH	001	01	EM	031	19
STX	002	02	SUB	032	1A
ETX	003	03	ESC	033	1B
EOT	004	04	FS(IS 4)	034	1C
ENQ	005	05	GS(IS 3)	035	1D
ACK	006	06	RS(IS 2)	036	1E
BEL	007	07	US(IS 1)	037	1F
BS(FE 0)	010	08	SPACE	040	20
HT(FE 1)	011	09	!	041	21
LF(FE 2)	012	0A	''	042	22
VT(FE 3)	013	0B	£ (‡)	043	23
FF(FE 4)	014	0C	$	044	24
CR(FE 5)	015	0D	%	045	25
SO	016	0E	&	046	26
SI	017	0F	'	047	27
DLE	020	10	(	050	28
DC1	021	11	)	051	29
DC2	022	12	*	052	2A
DC3	023	13	+	053	2B
DC4	024	14	,	054	2C
NAK	025	15			
SYN	026	16			
ETB	027	17			

ASCII CODES			ASCII CODES		
GRAPHIC	OCTAL	HEX	GRAPHIC	OCTAL	HEX
-	055	2D	Z	132	5A
.	056	2E	[	·133	5B
/	057	2F	\	134	5C
0	060	30	]	135	5D
1	061	31	∧	136	5E
2	062	32	—	137	5F
3	063	33	`	140	60
4	064	34	a	141	61
5	065	35	b	142	62
6	066	36	c	143	63
7	067	37	d	144	64
8	070	38	e	145	65
9	071	39	f	146	66
:	072	3A	g	147	67
;	073	3B	h	150	68
<	074	3C	i	151	69
=	075	3D	j	152	6A
>	076	3E	k	153	6B
?	077	3F	l	154	6C
@	100	40	m	155	6D
A	101	41	n	156	6E
B	102	42	o	157	6F
C	103	43	p	160	70
D	104	44	q	161	71
E	105	45	r	162	72
F	106	46	s	163	73
G	107	47	t	164	74
H	110	48	u	165	75
I	111	49	v	166	76
J	112	4A	w	167	77
K	113	4B	x	170	78
L	114	4C	y	171	79
M	115	4D	z	172	7A
N	116	4E	{	173	7B
O	117	4F	l	174	7C
P	120	50	}	175	7D
Q	121	51	~	176	7E
R	122	52	DEL	177	7F
S	123	53			
T	124	54			
U	125	55			
V	126	56			
W	127	57			
X	130	58			
Y	131	59			

CCITT NO. 2

BAUDOT CODE

CHARACTER		IMPULSE POSITION				
Lower Case	Upper Case	1	2	3	4	5
A	—	●	●			
B	?	●			●	●
C	:		●	●	●	
D	$	●			●	
E	3	●				
F	!	●		●	●	
G	&		●		●	●
H	£			●		●
I	8		●	●		
J	'	●	●		●	
K	(	●	●	●	●	
L	)		●			●
M	.			●	●	●
N	,			●	●	
O	9				●	●
P	0		●	●		●
Q	1	●	●	●		●
R	4		●		●	
S	Bell	●		●		
T	5					●
U	7	●	●	●		
V	;		●	●	●	●
W	2	●	●			●
X	/	●		●	●	●
Y	6	●		●		●
Z	"	●				●

CHARACTER		IMPULSE POSITION				
Lower Case	Upper Case	1	2	3	4	5
LETTERS (SHIFT TO LOWER CASE)		●	●	●	●	●
FIGURES (SHIFT TO UPPER CASE)		●	●		●	●
SPACE				●		
CARRIAGE RETURN					●	
LINE FEED			●			
BLANK						
PRESENCE OF ● INDICATES MARKING IMPULSE (MARK)						
ABSENCE OF ● INDICATES SPACING IMPULSE (SPACE)						

CCITT ALPHABET NO. 5
(ISO 7 BIT CODE ISO 646)

BASIC CODE TABLE

b_7				0	0	0	0	1	1	1	1
			b_6	0	0	1	1	0	0	1	1
			b_5	0	1	0	1	0	1	0	1
			column / row	0	1	2	3	4	5	6	7
b_4	b_3	b_2	b_1								
0	0	0	0	0	NUL	TC_7 (DLE)	SP	0	③	P	` ④	p
0	0	0	1	1	TC_1 (SOH)	DC_1	!	1	A	Q	a	q
0	0	1	0	2	TC_2 (STX)	DC_2	" ⑥	2	B	R	b	r
0	0	1	1	3	TC_3 (ETX)	DC_3	£(#) ②	3	C	S	c	s
0	1	0	0	4	TC_4 (EOT)	DC_4	$(¤) ②	4	D	T	d	t
0	1	0	1	5	TC_5 (ENQ)	TC_8 (NAK)	%	5	E	U	e	u
0	1	1	0	6	TC_6 (ACK)	TC_9 (SYN)	&	6	F	V	f	v
0	1	1	1	7	BEL	TC_{10} (ETB)	' ⑥	7	G	W	g	w
1	0	0	0	8	FE_0 (BS)	CAN	(	8	H	X	h	x
1	0	0	1	9	FE_1 (HT)	EM	)	9	I	Y	i	y
1	0	1	0	10	FE_2 (LF)①	SUB	*	:	J	Z	j	z
1	0	1	1	11	FE_3 (VT)①	ESC	+	;	K	③	k	③
1	1	0	0	12	FE_4 (FF)①	IS_4 (FS)	, ⑥	<	L	③	l	③
1	1	0	1	13	FE_5 (CR)①	IS_3 (GS)	-	=	M	③	m	③
1	1	1	0	14	SO	IS_2 (RS)	.	>	N	^ ④⑥	n	‾ ④⑤
1	1	1	1	15	SI	IS_1 (US)	/	?	O	_	o	DEL

NOTES ABOUT BASIC CODE TABLE

① The format effectors are intended for equipment in which horizontal and vertical movements are effected separately. If equipment requires the action of CARRIAGE RETURN to be combined with a vertical movement, the format effector for that vertical movement may be used to effect the combined movement. For example, if NEW LINE (symbol NL, equivalent to CR + LF) is required, FE_2 shall be used to represent it. This substitution requires agreement between the sender and the recipient of the data.

The use of these combined functions may be restricted for international transmission on general switched telecommunication networks (telegraph and telephone networks).

② The symbol £ is assigned to position 2/3 and the symbol $ is assigned to position 2/4. In a situation where there is no requirement for the symbol £ the symbol # (number sign) may be used in position 2/3. Where there is no requirement for the symbol $ the symbol ¤ (currency sign) may be used in position 2/4. The chosen allocations of symbols to these positions for international information interchange shall be agreed between the interested parties. It should be noted that, unless otherwise agreed between sender and recipient, the symbols £, $ or ¤ do not designate the currency of a specific country.

③ National use positions. The allocations of characters to these positions lies within the responsibility of national standardisation bodies. These positions are primarily intended for alphabet extensions. If they are not required for that purpose, they may be used for symbols.

④ Positions 5/14, 6/0 and 7/14 are provided for the symbols UPWARD ARROW HEAD, GRAVE ACCENT and OVERLINE. However, these positions may be used for other graphical characters when it is necessary to have 8, 9 or 10 positions for national use.

⑤ Position 7/14 is used for the graphic character ‾ (OVERLINE), the graphical representation of which may vary according to national use to represent ~ (TILDE) or another diacritical sign provided that there is no risk of confusion with another graphic character included in the table.

⑥ The graphic characters in positions 2/2, 2/7, 2/12 and 5/14 have respectively the significance of QUOTATION MARK, APOSTROPHE, COMMA and UPWARD ARROW HEAD; however, these characters take on the significance of the diacritical signs DIAERESIS, ACUTE ACCENT, CEDILLA and CIRCUMFLEX ACCENT when they are preceded or followed by the BACKSPACE character (0/8).

CONTROL CHARACTERS

Abbreviation	Note	Meaning	Position in the code table
ACK		Acknowledge	0/6
BEL		Bell	0/7
BS		Backspace	0/8
CAN		Cancel	1/8
CR	1	Carriage Return	0/13
DC		Device Control	—
DEL		Delete	7/15
DLE		Data Link Escape	1/0
EM		End of Medium	1/9
ENQ		Enquiry	0/5
EOT		End of Transmission	0/4
ESC		Escape	1/11
ETB		End of Transmission Block	1/7
ETX		End of Text	0/3
FE		Format Effector	—
FF	1	Form Feed	0/12
FS		File Separator	1/12
GS		Group Separator	1/13
HT		Horizontal Tabulation	0/9
IS		Information Separator	—
LF	1	Line Feed	0/10
NAK		Negative Acknowledge	1/5
NUL		Null	0/0
RS		Record Separator	1/14
SO		Shift-Out	0/14
SI		Shift-In	0/15
SOH		Start of Heading	0/1
SP		Space	2/0
STX		Start of Text	0/2
SUB		Substitute Character	1/10
SYN		Synchronous Idle	1/6
TC		Transmission Control	—
US		Unit Separator	1/15
VT	1	Vertical Tabulation	0/11

GRAPHIC CHARACTERS

Graphic	Note	Name	Position in the code table
(space)		Space	2/0
!		Exclamation mark	2/1
"	6	Quotation mark, Diaeresis	2/2
£	2	Pound sign	2/3
#	2	Number sign	2/3
$	2	Dollar sign	2/4
¤	2	Currency sign	2/4
%		Percent sign	2/5
&		Ampersand	2/6
'	6	Apostrophe, Acute accent	2/7
(		Left parenthesis	2/8
)		Right parenthesis	2/9
*		Asterisk	2/10
+		Plus sign	2/11
,	6	Comma, Cedilla	2/12
—		Hyphen, Minus sign	2/13
.		Full stop (period)	2/14
/		Solidus	2/15
:		Colon	3/10
;		Semi-colon	3/11
<		Less than sign	3/12
=		Equals sign	3/13
>		Greater than sign	3/14
?		Question mark	3/15
^	4, 6	Upward arrow head, Circumflex accent	5/14
		Underline	5/15
`	4	Grave accent	6/0
~	4, 5	Overline, Tilde	7/14

CCITT NO. 5

International reference version

b_4	b_3	b_2	b_1	b_7 / row	0	0	0	0	1	1	1	1
				b_6	0	0	1	1	0	0	1	1
				b_5	0	1	0	1	0	1	0	1
				column	0	1	2	3	4	5	6	7
0	0	0	0	0	NUL	TC$_7$ (DLE)	SP	0	@	P	`	p
0	0	0	1	1	TC$_1$ (SOH)	DC$_1$	!	1	A	Q	a	q
0	0	1	0	2	TC$_2$ (STX)	DC$_2$	"	2	B	R	b	r
0	0	1	1	3	TC$_3$ (ETX)	DC$_3$	#	3	C	S	c	s
0	1	0	0	4	TC$_4$ (EOT)	DC$_4$	¤	4	D	T	d	t
0	1	0	1	5	TC$_5$ (ENQ)	TC$_8$ (NAK)	%	5	E	U	e	u
0	1	1	0	6	TC$_6$ (ACK)	TC$_9$ (SYN)	&	6	F	V	f	v
0	1	1	1	7	BEL	TC$_{10}$ (ETB)	'	7	G	W	g	w
1	0	0	0	8	FE$_0$ (BS)	CAN	(	8	H	X	h	x
1	0	0	1	9	FE$_1$ (HT)	EM	)	9	I	Y	i	y
1	0	1	0	10	FE$_2$ (LF)	SUB	*	:	J	Z	j	z
1	0	1	1	11	FE$_3$ (VT)	ESC	+	;	K	[	k	{
1	1	0	0	12	FE$_4$ (FF)	IS$_4$ (FS)	,	<	L	\	l	|
1	1	0	1	13	FE$_5$ (CR)	IS$_3$ (GS)	-	=	M	]	m	}
1	1	1	0	14	SO	IS$_2$ (RS)	.	>	N	^	n	—
1	1	1	1	15	SI	IS$_1$ (US)	/	?	O	_	o	DEL

EBCDIC CODE

Decimal	Hexa-decimal	Graphic & Control Symbols EBCDIC	8-bit Code	Decimal	Hexa-decimal	Graphic & Control Symbols EBCDIC	8-bit Code
0	00	NUL	0000 0000	48	30		0011 0000
1	01	SOH	0000 0001	49	31		0011 0001
2	02	STX	0000 0010	50	32	SYN	0011 0010
3	03	ETX	0000 0011	51	33		0011 0011
4	04	PF	0000 0100	52	34	PN	0011 0100
5	05	HT	0000 0101	53	35	RS	0011 0101
6	06	LC	0000 0110	54	36	UC	0011 0110
7	07	DEL	0000 0111	55	37	EOT	0011 0111
8	08		0000 1000	56	38		0011 1000
9	09		0000 1001	57	39		0011 1001
10	0A	SMM	0000 1010	58	3A		0011 1010
11	0B.	VT	0000 1011	59	3B	CU3	0011 1011
12	0C	FF	0000 1100	60	3C	DC4	0011 1100
13	0D	CR	0000 1101	61	3D	NAK	0011 1101
14	0E	SO	0000 1110	62	3E		0011 1110
15	0F	SI	0000 1111	63	3F	SUB	0011 1111
16	10	DLE	0001 0000	64	40	SP	0100 0000
17	11	DC1	0001 0001	65	41		0100 0001
18	12	DC2	0001 0010	66	42		0100 0010
19	13	TM	0001 0011	67	43		0100 0011
20	14	RES	0001 0100	68	44		0100 0100
21	15	NL	0001 0101	69	45		0100 0101
22	16	BS	0001 0110	70	46		0100 0110
23	17	IL	0001 0111	71	47		0100 0111
24	18	CAN	0001 1000	72	48		0100 1000
25	19	EM	0001 1001	73	49		0100 1001
26	1A	CC	0001 1010	74	4A	¢	0100 1010
27	1B	CU1	0001 1011	75	4B	.	0100 1011
28	1C	IFS	0001 1100	76	4C	<	0100 1100
29	1D	IGS	0001 1101	77	4D	(	0100 1101
30	1E	IRS	0001 1110	78	4E	+	0100 1110
31	1F	IUS	0001 1111	79	4F	|	0100 1111
32	20	DS	0010 0000	80	50	&	0101 0000
33	21	SOS	0010 0001	81	51		0101 0001
34	22	FS	0010 0010	82	52		0101 0010
35	23		0010 0011	83	53		0101 0011
36	24	BYP	0010 0100	84	54		0101 0100
37	25	LF	0010 0101	85	55		0101 0101
38	26	ETB	0010 0110	86	56		0101 0110
39	27	ESC	0010 0111	87	57		0101 0111
40	28		0010 1000	88	58		0101 1000
41	29		0010 1001	89	59		0101 1001
42	2A	SM	0010 1010	90	5A	!	0101 1010
43	2B	CU2	0010 1011	91	5B	$	0101 1011
44	2C		0010 1100	92	5C	*	0101 1100
45	2D	ENQ	0010 1101	93	5D	)	0101 1101
46	2E	ACK	0010 1110	94	5E	;	0101 1110
47	2F	BEL	0010 1111	95	5F	¬	0101 1111

Decimal	Hexa-decimal	Graphic & Control Symbols EBCDIC	8-bit Code	Decimal	Hexa-decimal	Graphic & Control Symbols EBCDIC	8-bit Code
96	60	-	0110 0000	146	92	k	1001 0010
97	61	/	0110 0001	147	93	l	1001 0011
98	62		0110 0010	148	94	m	1001 0100
99	63		0110 0011	149	95	n	1001 0101
100	64		0110 0100	150	96	o	1001 0110
101	65		0110 0101	151	97	p	1001 0111
102	66		0110 0110	152	98	q	1001 1000
103	67		0110 0111	153	99	r	1001 1001
104	68		0110 1000	154	9A		1001 1010
105	69		0110 1001	155	9B		1001 1011
106	6A		0110 1010	156	9C		1001 1100
107	6B	,	0110 1011	157	9D		1001 1101
108	6C	%	0110 1100	158	9E		1001 1110
109	6D	—	0110 1101	159	9F		1001 1111
110	6E	>	0110 1110	160	A0		1010 0000
111	6F	?	0110 1111	161	A1		1010 0001
112	70		0111 0000	162	A2	s	1010 0010
113	71		0111 0001	163	A3	t	1010 0011
114	72		0111 0010	164	A4	u	1010 0100
115	73		0111 0011	165	A5	v	1010 0101
116	74		0111 0100	166	A6	w	1010 0110
117	75		0111 0101	167	A7	x	1010 0111
118	76		0111 0110	168	A8	y	1010 1000
119	77		0111 0111	169	A9	z	1010 1001
120	78		0111 1000	170	AA		1010 1010
121	79		0111 1001	171	AB		1010 1011
122	7A	:	0111 1010	172	AC		1010 1100
123	7B	#	0111 1011	173	AD		1010 1101
124	7C	@	0111 1100	174	AE		1010 1110
125	7D	'	0111 1101	175	AF		1010 1111
126	7E	=	0111 1110	176	B0		1011 0000
127	7F	"	0111 1111	177	B1		1011 0001
128	80		1000 0000	178	B2		1011 0010
129	81	a	1000 0001	179	B3		1011 0011
130	82	b	1000 0010	180	B4		1011 0100
131	83	c	1000 0011	181	B5		1011 0101
132	84	d	1000 0100	182	B6		1011 0110
133	85	e	1000 0101	183	B7		1011 0111
134	86	f	1000 0110	184	B8		1011 1000
135	87	g	1000 0111	185	B9		1011 1001
136	88	h	1000 1000	186	BA		1011 1010
137	89	i	1000 1001	187	BB		1011 1011
138	8A		1000 1010	188	BC		1011 1100
139	8B		1000 1011	189	BD		1011 1101
140	8C		1000 1100	190	BE		1011 1110
141	8D		1000 1101	191	BF		1011 1111
142	8E		1000 1110	192	C0		1100 0000
143	8F		1000 1111	193	C1	A	1100 0001
144	90		1001 0000	194	C2	B	1100 0010
145	91	j	1001 0001	195	C3	C	1100 0011

Decimal	Hexa-decimal	Graphic & Control Symbols EBCDIC	8-bit Code	Decimal	Hexa-decimal	Graphic & Control Symbols EBCDIC	8-bit Code
196	C4	D	1100 0100	226	E2	S	1110 0010
197	C5	E	1100 0101	227	E3	T	1110 0011
198	C6	F	1100 0110	228	E4	U	1110 0100
199	C7	G	1100 0111	229	E5	V	1110 0101
200	C8	H	1100 1000	230	E6	W	1110 0110
201	C9	I	1100 1001	231	E7	X	1110 0111
202	CA		1100 1010	232	E8	Y	1110 1000
203	CB		1100 1011	233	E9	Z	1110 1001
204	CC		1100 1100	234	EA		1110 1010
205	CD		1100 1101	235	EB		1110 1011
206	CE		1100 1110	236	EC		1110 1100
207	CF		1100 1111	237	ED		1110 1101
208	D0		1101 0000	238	EE		1110 1110
209	D1	J	1101 0001	239	EF		1110 1111
210	D2	K	1101 0010	240	F0	0	1111 0000
211	D3	L	1101 0011	241	F1	1	1111 0001
212	D4	M	1101 0100	242	F2	2	1111 0010
213	D5	N	1101 0101	243	F3	3	1111 0011
214	D6	O	1101 0110	244	F4	4	1111 0100
215	D7	P	1101 0111	245	F5	5	1111 0101
216	D8	Q	1101 1000	246	F6	6	1111 0110
217	D9	R	1101 1001	247	F7	7	1111 0111
218	DA		1101 1010	248	F8	8	1111 1000
219	DB		1101 1011	249	F9	9	1111 1001
220	DC		1101 1100	250	FA		1111 1010
221	DD		1101 1101	251	FB		1111 1011
222	DE		1101 1110	252	FC		1111 1100
223	DF		1101 1111	253	FD		1111 1101
224	E0		1110 0000	254	FE		1111 1110
225	E1		1110 0001	255	FF		1111 1111

EBCDIC CODE DEFINITIONS

NUL	Null	LF	Line Feed
PF	Punch Off	ETB	End of Transmission Block
HT	Horizontal Tab	SI	Shift In
LC	Lower Case	SMM	Start of Manual Message
DEL	Delete	DLE	Data Link Escape
RES	Restore	DC1	Device Control 1
NL	New Line	DC2	Device Control 2
BS	Backspace	DC3	Device Control 3
IL	Idle	DC4	Device Control 4
CC	Cursor Control	NAK	Negative Acknowledge
DS	Digit Select	SYN	Synchronous Idle
SOS	Start of Significance	CAN	Cancel
FS	Field Separator	PRE	Prefix (or ESC Escape)
BYP	Bypass	SM	Set Made

PN	Punch On	VT	Vertical Tabulation
RS	Reader Stop	FF	Form Feed
UC	Upper Case	SO	Shift Out
EOT	End of Transmission		
SP	Space	EM	End of Medium
SOH	Start of Heading	SUB	Substitute
STX	Start of Text	IGS	Information Group Separator
ETX	End of Text	IRS	Information Record Separator
ENQ	Enquiry	IUS	Information Unit Separator
ACK	Acknowledge	IFS	Information Field Separator
BEL	Bell		

SPECIAL GRAPHIC CHARACTERS

¢	Cent Sign	—	Minus Sign, Hyphen
.	Period, Decimal Point	/	Virgule
<	Less Than Sign	,	Comma
(	Left Parenthesis	%	Percent
+	Plus Sign Logical OR	__	Underscore
|	Vertical Bar	>	Greater Than Sign
&	Ampersand	?	Question Mark
!	Exclamation Point	:	Colon
$	Dollar Sign	#	Number Sign
*	Asterisk	@	At Sign
)	Right Parenthesis	'	Prime Apostrophe
;	Semicolon	"	Quotation Mark
¬	Logical NOT	=	Equal Sign

THE INTERNATIONAL MORSE CODE

A	di dah	N	dah dit	1	di dah dah dah dah
B	dah di di dit	O	dah dah dah	2	di di dah dah dah
C	dah di dah dit	P	di dah dah dit	3	di di di dah dah
D	dah di dit	Q	dah dah di dah	4	di di di di dah
E	dit	R	di dah dit	5	di di di di dit
F	di di dah dit	S	di di dit	6	dah di di di dit
G	dah dah dit	T	dah	7	dah dah di di dit
H	di di di dit	U	di di dah	8	dah dah dah di dit
I	di dit	V	di di di dah	9	dah dah dah dah dit
J	di dah dah dah	W	di dah dah	0	dah dah dah dah dah
K	dah di dah	X	dah di di dah		
L	di dah di dit	Y	dah di dah dah		
M	dah dah	Z	dah dah di dit		

Period	di dah di dah di dah
Comma	dah dah di di dah dah
Question mark	di di dah dah di dit
Error	di di di di di di di dit
Wait (AS)	di dah di di dit

End of message (AR)	di dah di dah dit
Proceed (K)	dah di dah
End of work (SK)	di di di dah di dah
Break (BK)	dah di di di dah di dah

MORSE CODE TIMING

The basic timing measurement is the dot pulse (dit), all other morse code timings are a function of this unit length:

dot length (dit)	one unit
dash length (dah)	three units
pause between elements of one character	one unit
pause between characters	three units
pause between words	seven units

NATIONAL LETTERS FOR USE IN LATIN MORSE CODES

Ä	di dah di dah
Æ	di dah di dah
Å	di dah dah di dah
A	di dah dah di dah
CH	dah dah dah dah
É	di di dah di dit
N	dah dah di dah dah
Ö	dah dah dah dit
Ø	dah dah dah dit
Ü	di di dah dah

THE CYRILLIC CCITT2 CODE WITH THIRD SHIFT

1		1	2	3	4	5	6	7	8	9	10	11	12	13	14	15	16	17	18	19	20	21	22	23	24	25	26	27	28	29	30	31	32
2		А	Б	Ц	Д	Е	Ф	Г	Х	И	Й	К	Л	М	Н	О	П	Я	Р	С	Т	У	Ж	В	Ь	Ы	З						
3		–	?	:	✠	3	З	Ш	Щ	8	10	(	)	.	,	9	0	1	у	’	5	7	=	2	/	6	+						
4		A	B	C	D	E	F	G	H	I	J	K	L	M	N	O	P	Q	R	S	T	U	V	W	X	Y	Z	<	≡	A...	1...	Zwr	←
5		–	?	:	✠	3				8	⍾	(	)	.	,	9	0	1	4,	’	5	7	=	2	/	6	+						
6																																	
7	1	●	●		●	●	●				●	●						●		●		●		●	●	●	●			●	●		
	2	●		●				●		●	●	●	●				●	●	●			●	●	●					●	●	●		
	3			●			●		●	●		●		●	●		●	●		●		●	●		●	●				●		●	
	4		●	●	●		●	●			●	●		●	●	●			●				●		●			●		●	●		
	5		●					●	●				●	●		●	●	●			●		●	●	●	●	●			●	●		
8		●	●	●	●	●	●	●	●	●	●	●	●	●	●	●	●	●	●	●	●	●	●	●	●	●	●	●	●	●	●	●	●

1 No. of code combination in International Telegraph Code No. 2
2 Letters
3 Figures
4 Letters
5 Figures
6 Start pulse
7 Code elements
8 Stop pulse

□ No-current pulse } with neutral current operation
● Current pulse } with neutral current operation

< Carriage return

≡ Line feed

← shift to national alphabet

✠ Who are you?

◹ Free for domestic traffic in each country

⍾ Bell

1 ... Figures shift

A... Letters shift

ZWR Space

THE GREEK CCITT2 CODE WITH THIRD SHIFT

No.	1	2	3	4	5	6	7	8	9	10	11	12	13	14	15	16	17	18	19	20	21	22	23	24	25	26	27	28	29	30	31	32
2 Letters	Α	Β	Ψ	Δ	Ε	Φ	Γ	Η	Ι	Ξ	Κ	Λ	Μ	Ν	Ο	Π	□	Ρ	Σ	Τ	Θ	Ω	□	Χ	Υ	Ζ						
3 Figures	-	?	:	✠	3	°	%	□	8	⌐	(	)	.	,	9	0	1	4	'	5	7	=	2	/	6	+	∨	≡	A...	1...	Zwr	↓
5 Letters	A	B	C	D	E	F	G	H	I	J	K	L	M	N	O	P	Q	R	S	T	U	V	W	X	Y	Z						
6 Start pulse																																
7 el 1	●	●		●	●	●				●	●						●		●		●		●	●	●	●			●	●		
7 el 2	●		●				●		●	●	●	●				●	●	●			●	●	●					●	●	●		
7 el 3			●			●		●	●		●		●	●		●	●		●		●	●		●	●				●		●	
7 el 4		●	●	●		●	●			●	●		●	●	●			●				●		●			●		●	●		
7 el 5		●					●	●				●	●		●	●				●		●	●	●	●	●			●	●		
8 Stop pulse	●	●	●	●	●	●	●	●	●	●	●	●	●	●	●	●	●	●	●	●	●	●	●	●	●	●	●	●	●	●	●	●

1 No. of code combination in International Telegraph Code No. 2
2 Letters
3 Figures
5 Letters
6 Start pulse
7 Code elements
8 Stop pulse

□ No-current pulse ⎫
● Current pulse ⎬ with neutral current operation
          ⎭

∨ Carriage return
≡ Line feed
↓ shift to national alphabet

✠ Who are you?
□ Free for domestic traffic in each country

⌐ Bell
1... Figures shift
A... Letters shift
ZWR Space

2 Miscellaneous Codes

TELEX ANSWERBACK COUNTRY IDENTIFIERS

ABU DHABI (United Arab	EM	COLOMBIA	CO
Emirates)		COMORO ISLANDS	KO
AFGHANISTAN	AF	CONGO (People's Republic)	KG
AJMAN (United Arab Emirates)	EM	COOK (Hervey) Islands	RG
ALASKA	UA	COSTA RICA	CR
ALBANIA	AB	CUBA	CU
ALGERIA	DZ	CYPRUS	CY
AMERICAN SAMOA	AS	CZECHOSLAVAKIA	C
ANDORRA	AND	DENMARK	DK
ANGOLA	AN	DJIBOUTI	DJ
ANGUILLA	LA	DOMINICA	DO
ANTIGUA	AK	DOMINICAN REPUBLIC	
ANTILLES	NA	– RCA	DR
(Netherlands)		– AACR (ITT)	DI
ARGENTINA	AR	DUBAI United Arab Emirates	EM
ASCENSION ISLAND	AV	ECUADOR	ED
AUSTRALIA	AA	EGYPT	UN
AUSTRIA	A	EL SALVADOR	SR
BAHAMAS	BS	ETHIOPIA	ET
BAHRAIN	BN	FALKLAND ISLANDS	FK
BANGLADESH	BJ	FAROE ISLANDS	FA
BARBADOS	WB	FIJI	FJ
BELGIUM	B	FINLAND	SF
BELIZE	BZ	FRANCE	F
BENIN	DY	(incl. Monaco)	
BERMUDA	BA	FRENCH ANTILLES:	
BOLIVIA		Guadeloupe	GL
Nos beginning 2, 3, 4, & 6	BV	Martinique	MR
Nos beginning 5	BX	FRENCH GUIANA	FG
BOTSWANA	BD	FRENCH POLYNESIA	FP
BRAZIL	BR	FUJAIRAH (United Arab Emirates)	EM
BRUNEI	BU	GABON	GO
BULGARIA	BG	GAMBIA	GV
BURMA	BM	GERMAN DEMOCRATIC	
BURUNDI	UU	REPUBLIC	DD
CAMEROON	KN	GERMANY, FEDERAL	
CANADA	CA	REPUBLIC of	D
CAPE VERDE	CV	GHANA	GH
CAYMAN ISLANDS	CP	GIBRALTAR	GK
CENTRAL AFRICAN EMPIRE	EC	GREECE	GR
CHAD	KD	(incl. Crete)	
CHILE		GREENLAND	GD
– TRA	CK	GRENADA	GA
– TDE	CL	GUADELOUPE	GL
– ITT	CZ	GUATEMALA	GU
– TEXCOM	CT	GUINEA	GE
CHINA (People's Republic)	CN	GUINEA-BISSAU	BI

GUYANA	GY	NEW CALEDONIA	NM
HAITI	HI	NEW HEBRIDES	
HAWAII		(Vanuatu)	NH
– ITT	HM	NEW ZEALAND	NZ
– RCA	HR	NICARAGUA	NU
– WUI	HW	NIGER	NI
HONDURAS	HO	NIGERIA	NG
HONG KONG	HX	NORTH KOREA	KP
HUNGARY	H	NORWAY	N
ICELAND	IS	OMAN	MB
INDIA	IN	PAKISTAN	PK
INDONESIA	IA	PANAMA	
IRAN	IR	– TRT	PA
IRAQ	IK	– Intel & AACR (ITT)	PG
IRISH REPUBLIC	EI	PAPUA NEW GUINEA	NE
ISRAEL	IL	PARAGUAY	PY
ITALY	I	PERU	PE
IVORY COAST	CI	PHILIPIPPINES	
JAMAICA	JA	– PHILCOM (RCA)	PH
JAPAN	J	– ETPI	PN
JORDAN	JO	– GMC	PM
KENYA	KE	– PTT	PU
KOREA (People's Democratic		– CAPWIRE	PS
Republic)	KP	POLAND	PL
KOREA (Republic of South		PORTUGAL	P
Korea)	K	(Incl. Azores and Madeira)	
KUWAIT	KT	PUERTO RICO	
LAOS	LS	– AACR (ITT)	PD
LEBANON	LE	– CW/WUI	PP
LESOTHO	BB	– RCA	PT
LIBERIA	LI	QATAR	DH
LIBYA	LY	RAS AL KHAIMAH (United	
LIECHTENSTEIN	FL	Arab Emirates)	EM
LUXEMBOURG	LU	REUNION	RE
MACAO	OM	ROMANIA	R
MADAGASCAR	MG	RWANDA	RW
MALAWI	MI	SAINT HELENA	HL
MALAYSIA	MA	SAINT KITTS-NEVIS	KC
MALDIVE ISLANDS	MF	SAINT LUCIA	LC
MALI	MJ	SAINT PIERRE and MIQUELON	QN
MALTA	MW	SAINT VICENT	VQ
MARIANA ISLANDS	MN	SAMOA (USA territory)	SB
MARTINIQUE	MR	SAMOA (Western)	SX
MAURITANIA	MQ	SAN MARINO	I
MAURITIUS	IW	SÃO TOMÉ and PRINCIPE	ST
MEXICO	ME	SAUDI ARABIA	SJ
MONGOLIA	MH	SENEGAL	SG
MONTSERRAT	MK	SEYCHELLES	SZ
MOROCCO	M	SHARAJAH (United Arab	
MOZAMBIQUE	MO	Emirates)	EM
NAMIBIA (South West Africa)	WK	SIERRA LEONE	SL
NAURU ISLAND	ZV	SINGAPORE	RS
NEPAL	NP	SOLOMON ISLANDS	HQ
NETHERLANDS	NL	SOMALI DEMOCRATIC	
NETHERLANDS ANTILLES	NA	REPUBLIC	SM

SOUTH AFRICA	SA	UNITED ARAB EMIRATES	EM
SOUTH KOREA	K	UNITED KINGDOM	G
SPAIN	E	UPPER VOLTA	UV
(incl. Canary and Balearic Islands)		URUGUAY	UY
SRI LANKA	CE	U.S.A.	
SUDAN	SD	– WU	UD
SURINAM	SN	– TWX	UQ
SWAZILAND	WD	– RCA	UR
SWEDEN	S	– ITT	UI
SWITZERLAND	CH	– WUI	UW
SYRIA	SY	– FTCC	UF
TAIWAN	TA	– TRT	UT
TANZANIA	TA	U.S.S.R.	SU
THAILAND	TH	VATICAN CITY	VA
TOBAGO	WG	VENEZUELA	VE
TOGO	TO	VIETNAM	VT
TONGA	TS	VIRGIN ISLANDS (U.S.A.)	VN
TORTOLA	VB	VIRGIN ISLANDS (British)	VB
(British Virgin Islands)		WALLIS and FUTUNA ISLANDS	WF
TRANSKEI	TT	WESTERN SAMOA	SX
TRINIDAD	WG	YEMEN ARAB REPUBLIC	YE
TUNISIA	TN	YEMEN (People's Democratic	AD
TURKEY	TR	Republic)	
TURKS and CAICOS ISLANDS	TO	YUGOSLAVIA	YU
UGANDA	UG	ZAIRE	ZR
UMM AL QUWAIN (United		ZAMBIA	ZA
Arab Emirates)	EM	ZIMBABWE	RH

SYMBOLS DESIGNATING COUNTRIES OR GEOGRAPHICAL AREAS (AS DEFINED BY ITU)

AAA	Shared throughout the world	BER	Bermuda
AAB	Shared by several countries, but in	BGD	Bangladesh
	a restricted area of the world	BHR	Bahrain
ADL	Adélie Land	BIO	British Indian Ocean Territory
AFG	Afghanistan	BLR	Byelorussia
AFS	South Africa (Republic of)	BOL	Bolivia
AGL	Angola	BOT	Botswana
ALB	Albania	BRB	Barbados
ALG	Algeria	BRM	Burma
ALS	Alaska	BRU	Brunei
AMS	Saint Paul and Amsterdam Islands	BUL	Bulgaria
AND	Andorra	CAF	Central African Republic
AOE	Spanish Sahara Territory	CAN	Canada
ARG	Argentina	CAR	Caroline Islands
ARS	Saudi Arabia	CBG	Kampuchea
ASC	Ascension	CHL	Chile
ATN	Netherlands Antilles	CHN	China
AUS	Australia	CHR	Christmas Island
AUT	Azores	CKH	Cook Islands
B	Brazil	CKN	Cook Islands (Northern Group)
BAH	Bahamas	CLM	Colombia
BDI	Burundi	CLN	Sri Lanka
BEL	Belgium	CME	Cameroon
BEN	Benin	CNR	Canaries

COG   Congo
COM   Comoro Islands
CPV   Cape Verde
CRO   Crozet Archipelago
CTI   Ivory Coast
CTR   Costa Rica
CUB   Cuba
CVA   Vatican City State
CYP   Cyprus
D   Germany (Federal Republic of)
DDR   German Democratic Republic
DJI   Djibouti
DMA   Dominica
DNK   Denmark
DOM   Dominican Republic
E   Spain
ECD   Communication-satellite space station(s) for use by URS
ECE   Communication-satellite space station(s) for use by USA
ECF   Communication-satellite space station(s) for use by URS
ECH   Communication-satellite space station(s) for use by BEL
ECI   Communication-satellite space station(s) for use by USA
ECJ   Communication-satellite space station(s) for use by USA
ECL   Communication-satellite space station(s) for use by F
EGY   Egypt
EHA   Space research space station(s) for use by CAN
EHC   Space research space station(s) for use by F
EHE   Space research space station(s) for use by USA
EHF   Space research space station(s) for use by CAN
EHK   Space research space station(s) for use by F
EHM   Space research space station(s) for use by CAN
EHN   Space research space station(s) for use by F
EHO   Space research space station(s) for use by F
EHP   Space research space station(s) for use by F
EHR   Space research space station(s) for use by USA
EHT   Space research space station(s) for use by USA
EMA   Meteorological-satellite space station(s) for use by URS

EMB   Meteorological-satellite space station(s) for use by USA
EMC   Meteorological-satellite space station(s) for use by F
EMD   Meteorological-satellite space station(s) for use by USA
ENA   Radionavigation-satellite space station(s) for use by USA
EQA   Ecuador
ETH   Ethiopia
F   France
FJI   Fiji
FLK   Falkland Islands and Dependencies
FNL   Finland
G   United Kingdom of Great Britain and Northern Ireland
GAB   Gabon
GCA   Territories in the United Kingdom in Region 1
GCB   Territories in the United Kingdom in Region 2
GCC   Territories in the United Kingdom in Region 3
GDL   Guadeloupe
GHA   Ghana
GIB   Gibraltar
GMB   Gambia
GNB   Guinea-Bissau
GNE   Equatorial Guinea
GRC   Greece
GRL   Greenland
GTM   Guatemala
GUB   Guyana
GUF   Guyana (French Department of)
GUI   Guinea
GUM   Guam
HKG   Hong Kong
HNB   Belize
HND   Honduras
HNG   Hungary
HOL   Netherlands
HTI   Haiti
HVO   Upper Volta
HWA   Hawaii
HWL   Howland Island
I   Italy
ICO   Cocos Keeling Islands
IND   India
INS   Indonesia
IOB   British West Indies
IRL   Ireland
IRN   Iran
IRQ   Iraq
ISL   Iceland
ISR   Israel

J	Japan		India and Pakistan'
JAR	Jarvis Island	ONJ	Stations of the 'United Nations
JMC	Jamaica		Truce Supervision Organisation in
JON	Johnston Island		areas between the Armistice
JOR	Jordan		Demarcation Lines at Jerusalem'
KEN	Kenya	PAK	Pakistan
KER	Kerguelen Islands	PAQ	Easter Island
KIR	Kiribati	PHL	Philippines
KOR	Korea (Republic of)	PHX	Phoenix Islands
KRE	Korea (Democratic People's	PLM	Palmyra Island
	Republic of)	PNG	Papua New Guinea
KWT	Kuwait	PNR	Panama (Republic of)
LAO	Laos	PNZ	Panama Canal Zone
LBN	Lebanon	POL	Poland
LBR	Liberia	POR	Portugal
LBY	Libya	PRG	Paraguay
LCA	Saint Lucia	PRU	Peru
LIE	Liechtenstein	PTC	Pitcairn Island
LSO	Lesotho	PTR	Puerto Rico
LUX	Luxembourg	QAT	Qatar
MAC	Macao	REU	Reunion
MAU	Mauritius	ROD	Rodriguez
MCO	Monaco	ROU	Romania
MDG	Madagascar	RRW	Rwanda
MDR	Madeira	S	Sweden
MDW	Midway Islands	SDN	Sudan
MEX	Mexico	SEN	Senegal
MLA	Malaysia	SEY	Seychelles
MLD	Maldives	SHN	Saint Helena
MLI	Mali	SLM	Solomon Islands
MLT	Malta	SLV	El Salvador
MNG	Mongolia	SMA	American Samoa
MOZ	Mozambique	SMO	Western Samoa
MRA	Mariana Islands	SMR	San Marino
MRC	Morocco	SNG	Singapore
MRL	Marshall Islands	SOM	Somalia
MRN	Marion Island	SPM	Saint Pierre and Miquelon
MRT	Martinique	SRL	Sierra Leone
MTN	Mauritania	STP	São Tomé and Principe
MWI	Malawi	SUI	Switzerland
MYT	Mayotte Island	SUR	Surinam
NCG	Nicaragua	SWN	Swan Island
NCL	New Caledonia and Dependencies	SWZ	Swaziland
NGR	Niger	SYR	Syria
NIG	Nigeria	TCD	Chad
NIU	Niue Island	TCH	Czechoslovakia
NMB	Namibia	TGK	Tanzania (Tanganyika)
NOR	Norway	TGO	Togo
NPL	Nepal	THA	Thailand
NRU	Nauru Island	TKL	Tokelau Islands
NZL	New Zealand	TMP	Portuguese Timor
OCE	French Polynesia	TON	Tonga
OMA	Oman	TRC	Tristan da Cunha
ONC	Stations of the 'United Nations	TRD	Trinidad and Tobago
	Military Observer Group in	TUN	Tunisia

TUR	Turkey	VUT	Vanuatu
TUV	Tuvalu	WAK	Wake Island
UAE	United Arab Emirates	WAL	Wallis and Futuna Islands
UGA	Uganda	YEM	Yemen Arab Republic
UKR	Ukrainian Republic	YMS	Yemen (People's Democratic
URG	Uruguay		Republic of)
URS	U.S.S.R.	YUG	Yugoslavia
USA	U.S.A.	ZAI	Zaire
VEN	Venezuela	ZAN	Tanzania (Zanzibar)
VIR	Virgin Islands	ZMB	Zambia
VTN	Vietnam	ZWE	Zimbabwe

U.S. AREA CODE DIRECTORY

ALPHABETICAL

ALABAMA		**ILLINOIS**	
All Points	205	Centralia	618
ALASKA		Chicago	312
All Points	907	Peoria	309
ARIZONA		Rockford	815
All Points	602	Springfield	217
ARKANSAS		**INDIANA**	
All Points	501	Evansville	612
CALIFORNIA		Indianapolis	317
Bakersfield	805	South Bend	219
Fresno	209	**IOWA**	
Los Angeles	213	Cedar Rapids	319
Sacramento	916	Council Bluffs	712
San Diego	714	Des Moines	515
San Francisco	415	**KANSAS**	
San Jose	408	Topeka	913
Santa Rosa	707	Wichita	316
COLORADO		**KENTUCKY**	
All Points	303	Ashland	606
CONNECTICUT		Frankfort	502
All Points	203	Louisville	502
DELAWARE		**LOUISIANA**	
All Points	302	Baton Rouge	504
DISTRICT OF COLUMBIA		New Orleans	504
All Points	202	Shreveport	318
FLORIDA		**MAINE**	
Jacksonville	904	All Points	207
Miami	305	**MARYLAND**	
Orlando	305	All Points	301
St Petersburg	813	**MASSACHUSETTS**	
Tallahassee	904	Boston	617
Tampa	813	Falmouth	617
GEORGIA		Lowell	617
Atlanta	404	Springfield	413
Savannah	912	Worcester	617
HAWAII		**MICHIGAN**	
All Points	808	Detroit	313
IDAHO		Escanaba	906
All Points	208	Grand Rapids	616
		Lansing	517

MINNESOTA			NORTH DAKOTA	
Duluth	218		All Points	701
Minneapolis	612		OHIO	
Rochester	507		Akron	216
MISSISSIPPI			Cincinnati	513
All Points	601		Cleveland	216
MISSOURI			Columbus	614
Jefferson City	314		Dayton	513
Kansas City	816		Toledo	419
St Louis	314		Youngstown	216
Springfield	417		OKLAHOMA	
MONTANA			Oklahoma City	405
All Points	406		Tulsa	918
NEBRASKA			OREGON	
Lincoln	402		All Points	503
North Platte	308		PENNSYLVANIA	
Omaha	402		Allentown (Lehigh Co.)	215
NEVADA			Altoona	814
All Points	702		Easton	215
NEW HAMPSHIRE			Erie	814
All Points	603		Harrisburg	717
NEW JERSEY			Johnstown	814
Atlantic City	609		Lancaster	717
Camden	609		Morrisville (Bucks Co.)	215
Newark	201		New Hope	215
Paterson	201		Philadelphia	215
Trenton	609		Pittsburgh	412
NEW MEXICO			Reading	215
All Points	505		Scranton	717
NEW YORK			Wilkes-Barre	717
Albany	518		Williamsport	215
Binghampton	607		Yardley	215
Buffalo	716		York	717
Elmira	607		RHODE ISLAND	
Garden City	516		All Points	401
Greenport (Col Co.)	518		SOUTH CAROLINA	
Hampstead	516		All Points	803
Ithaca	607		SOUTH DAKOTA	
Mt Vernon	914		All Points	605
Newburgh	914		TENNESSEE	
New York City	212		Chattanooga	615
Nyack	914		Memphis	901
Poughkeepsie	914		Nashville	615
Riverhead	516		TEXAS	
Rochester	716		Amarillo	806
Saratoga Springs	518		Austin	512
Syracuse	315		Dallas	214
Utica	315		El Paso	915
White Plains	914		Fort Worth	817
NORTH CAROLINA			Houston	713
Asheville	704		San Antonio	512
Charlotte	704		UTAH	
Fayetteville	919		All Points	801
Raleigh	919		VERMONT	
Winston-Salem	919		All Points	802

VIRGINIA			Spokane	509
Arlington	703		WEST VIRGINIA	
Charlottesville	804		All Points	304
Norfolk	804		WISCONSIN	
Richmond	804		Madison	608
Roanoke	703		Milwaukee	414
WASHINGTON			Superior	715
Olympia	206		WYOMING	
Seattle	206		All Points	307

Canada, Mexico and the Caribbean

BAHAMAS			Windsor	519
All Points	809		Quebec	
CANADA			Montreal	514
Alberta	403		Quebec	418
British Columbia	604		Trois Rivières	819
Manitoba	204		Saskatchewan	309
New Brunswick	506		MEXICO	
Newfoundland	709		Mexico City	905
Nova Scotia	902		Northwest Area	903
Ontario			Southern Area	905
Fort William	807		PUERTO RICO	
Ottawa	613		All Points	809
Sault Marie	705		VIRGIN ISLANDS	
Toronto	416		All Points	809

NUMERICAL

State or Province	Area		State or Province	Area
201 NEW JERSEY	NEWARK		217 ILLINOIS	SPRINGFIELD
	PATERSON		218 MINNESOTA	DULUTH
202 WASHINGTON	ALL POINTS		219 INDIANA	SOUTH BEND
D.C.			301 MARYLAND	ALL POINTS
203 CONNECTICUT	ALL POINTS		302 DELAWARE	ALL POINTS
204 MANITOBA	ALL POINTS		303 COLORADO	ALL POINTS
205 ALABAMA	ALL POINTS		304 WEST VIRGINIA	ALL POINTS
206 WASHINGTON	SEATTLE		305 FLORIDA	MIAMI
	OLYMPIA			ORLANDO
207 MAINE	ALL POINTS		306 SASKATCHEWAN	ALL POINTS
208 IDAHO	ALL POINTS		307 WYOMING	ALL POINTS
209 CALIFORNIA	FRESNO		308 NEBRASKA	NORTH PLATTE
212 NEW YORK	NEW YORK CITY		309 ILLINOIS	PEORIA
213 CALIFORNIA	LOS ANGELES		312 ILLINOIS	CHICAGO
214 TEXAS	DALLAS		313 MICHIGAN	DETROIT
215 PENNSYLVANIA	ALLENTOWN		314 MISSOURI	ST LOUIS
	EASTON			JEFFERSON
	MORRISVILLE			CITY
	NEW HOPE		315 NEW YORK	SYRACUSE
	PHILADELPHIA			UTICA
	READING		316 KANSAS	WICHITA
	YARDLEY			
216 OHIO	AKRON			
	CLEVELAND			
	YOUNGSTOWN			

State or Province	Area	State or Province	Area
317 INDIANA	INDIANAPOLIS	606 KENTUCKY	ASHLAND
318 LOUISIANA	SHREVEPORT		COVINGTON
319 IOWA	CEDAR RAPIDS	607 NEW YORK	BINGHAMTON
401 RHODE ISLAND	ALL POINTS		ELMIRA
402 NEBRASKA	LINCOLN		ITHACA
	OMAHA	608 WISCONSIN	MADISON
403 ALBERTA	ALL POINTS	609 NEW JERSEY	CAMDEN
404 GEORGIA	ALL POINTS		TRENTON
405 OKLAHOMA	OKLAHOMA		ATLANTIC CITY
	CITY	610 4 ROW TWX	CANADA
406 MONTANA	ALL POINTS	612 MINNESOTA	MINNEAPOLIS
408 CALIFORNIA	SAN JOSE	613 ONTARIO	OTTAWA
412 PENNSYLVANIA	PITTSBURGH	614 OHIO	COLUMBUS
413 MASSACHUSETTS	SPRINGFIELD	615 TENNESSEE	CHATTANOOGA
414 WISCONSIN	MILWAUKEE		NASHVILLE
415 CALIFORNIA	SAN FRANCISCO	616 MICHIGAN	GRAND RAPIDS
416 ONTARIO	TORONTO	617 MASSACHUSETTS	BOSTON
417 MISSOURI	SPRINGFIELD		LOWELL
418 QUEBEC	QUEBEC		WORCESTER
419 OHIO	TOLEDO		FALMOUTH
501 ARKANSAS	ALL POINTS	618 ILLINOIS	CENTRALIA
502 KENTUCKY	LOUISVILLE	701 NORTH DAKOTA	ALL POINTS
	FRANKFORT	702 NEVADA	ALL POINTS
503 OREGON	ALL POINTS	703 VIRGINIA	ARLINGTON
504 LOUISIANA	BATON ROUGE		ROANOKE
	NEW ORLEANS	704 NORTH	
505 NEW MEXICO	ALL POINTS	CAROLINA	CHARLOTTE
506 NEW			ASHEVILLE
BRUNSWICK	ALL POINTS	705 ONTARIO	NORTH BAY
507 MINNESOTA	ROCHESTER	707 CALIFORNIA	SANTA ROSA
509 WASHINGTON	SPOKANE	709 NEWFOUND-	
510 4 ROW TWX	U.S.A.	LAND	ALL POINTS
512 TEXAS	AUSTIN	710 4 ROW TWX	U.S.A.
	SAN ANTONIO	712 IOWA	COUNCIL
513 OHIO	CINCINNATI		BLUFFS
	DAYTON	713 TEXAS	HOUSTON
514 QUEBEC	MONTREAL	714 CALIFORNIA	SAN DIEGO
515 IOWA	DES MOINES	715 WISCONSIN	SUPERIOR
516 NEW YORK	GARDEN CITY	716 NEW YORK	ROCHESTER
	HAMPSTEAD		BUFFALO
	RIVERHEAD	717 PENNSYLVANIA	HARRISBURG
517 MICHIGAN	LANSING		LANCASTER
518 NEW YORK	ALBANY		WILKES-BARRE
	GREENPORT		SCRANTON
	SARATOGA		YORK
	SPRINGS	800 INWARD WATS	ALL STATES
519 ONTARIO	LONDON	801 UTAH	ALL POINTS
	WINDSOR	802 VERMONT	ALL POINTS
601 MISSISSIPPI	ALL POINTS	803 SOUTH	
602 ARIZONA	ALL POINTS	CAROLINA	ALL POINTS
603 NEW HAMPSHIRE	ALL POINTS	804 VIRGINIA	CHARLOTTES-
604 BRITISH			VILLE
COLUMBIA	ALL POINTS		NORFOLK
605 SOUTH DAKOTA	ALL POINTS		RICHMOND

State or Province	Area	State or Province	Area
805 CALIFORNIA	BAKERSFIELD	902 NOVA SCOTIA	ALL POINTS
806 TEXAS	AMARILLO	PRINCE EDWARD	
807 ONTARIO	FORT WILLIAM	ISLAND	ALL POINTS
808 HAWAII	ALL POINTS	903 MEXICO	NORTHWEST
809 CARIBBEAN	BAHAMAS	904 FLORIDA	JACKSONVILLE
	PUERTO RICO		TALLAHASSEE
	VIRGIN	905 MEXICO	MEXICO CITY
	ISLANDS	906 MICHIGAN	ESCANABA
	BERMUDA	907 ALASKA	ALL POINTS
810 4 ROW TWX	U.S.A.	910 4 ROW TWX	U.S.A.
812 INDIANA	EVANSVILLE	912 GEORGIA	SAVANNAH
813 FLORIDA	TAMPA	913 KANSAS	TOPEKA
	ST PETERS-	914 NEW YORK	MOUNT
	BURG		VERNON
814 PENNSYLVANIA	ALTOONA		NEWBURGH
	ERIE		NYACK
	JOHNSTOWN	915 TEXAS	EL PASO
815 ILLINOIS	ROCKFORD		SWEETWATER
816 MISSOURI	KANSAS CITY	916 CALIFORNIA	SACRAMENTO
817 TEXAS	FORT WORTH	918 OKLAHOMA	TULSA
819 QUEBEC	TROIS	919 NORTH	
	RIVIÈRES	CAROLINA	RALEIGH
901 TENNESSEE	MEMPHIS		WINSTON-
			SALEM

Q CODES

(ITU RADIO REGULATIONS, 1982, APPENDICES 13 and 14)

The series listed here (QRA to QUZ) is for general use. The series QAA to QNZ is for use by the aeronautical service and the series QOA to QQZ is for use by the maritime service.

QRA   The name of this station is . . .
QRB   The approximate distance between us is . . . nautical miles (or kilometres).
QRC   Charges to my station are settled by . . .
QRD   I am bound for . . .
QRE   My estimated time of arrival is . . .
QRF   I am returning to . . .
QRG   Your frequency is . . . kHz.
QRH   Your frequency varies.
QRJ   I have . . . radio telephone calls to book.
QRK   The intelligibility of your signals is:
       1 bad
       2 poor
       .3 fair
       4 good
       5 excellent
QRL   I am busy.
QRM   I have interference.
QRN   I am troubled by static.
QRO   Increase transmitter power.
QRP   Decrease transmitter power.

QRQ   Send faster.
QRR   I am ready for auto operation.
QRS   Send slower.
QRT   Stop sending.
QRU   I have nothing for you.
QRV   I am ready.
QRW   Please inform . . . that I am calling him.
QRX   I will call again at . . . hours.
QRY   Your turn is number . . .
QRZ   You are being called by . . .
QSA   The strength of your signals is:
        1 scarcely perceptible
        2 weak
        3 fair
        4 good
        5 very good
QSB   Your signals are fading.
QSC   I am a cargo vessel.
QSD   Your keying is defective.
QSE   The estimated drift of the craft is . . .
QSF   I have effected rescue and am proceeding to . . .
QSG   Send . . . at a time.
QSH   I can home on my DF equipment.
QSI   I cannot break into your transmissions.
QSJ   The charge to be collected is . . .
QSK   I can hear you between my signals – break-in.
QSL   I am acknowledging receipt.
QSM   Repeat telegram number . . .
QSN   I heard you on . . . kHz.
QSO   I can communicate with . . . direct.
QSP   I will relay to . . .
QSQ   I have a doctor on board.
QSR   Repeat on the calling frequency.
QSS   I will use the working frequency . . . kHz.
QSU   Reply on this frequency.
QSV   Send a series of V's.
QSW   I will send on this frequency.
QSX   I am listing to . . .
QSY   Change frequency.
QSZ   Send each word or group twice.
QTA   Cancel telegram number . . .
QTB   I disagree with your total.
QTC   I have . . . messages for you.
QTD   . . . has recovered . . . survivors.
QTE   The true bearing of . . . was . . . degrees.
QTF   Your position is . . .
QTG   I will send two ten-second dashes followed by my call sign.
QTH   My position is . . .
QTI   My true track is . . .
QTJ   My speed is . . . km per hour.

QRK   My air speed is . . . knots.
QTL   My true heading is . . .
QTM   My magnetic heading is . . .
QTO   I have left.
QTP   I am about to alight or land.
QTQ   I am about to call you.
QTR   The correct time is . . . hours.
QTS   Please measure my frequency.
QTT   My Id is superimposed on another signal.
QTU   My station is open from . . . to . . . hours.
QTV   Keep . . . kHz free for me.
QTW   Survivors need . . .
QTX   I will keep my station open until further notice.
QTY   I am proceeding to the incident and expect to arrive at . . . hours.
QTZ   I am continuing to search.
QUA   Here is news of . . .
QUB   Here is the information requested.
QUC   The last message I received from you was number . . .
QUD   I have received an urgency signal from . . .
QUE   I can use telephony on . . . kHz.
QUF   I have received a distress signal from . . . at . . . hours.
QUG   I shall be forced to land at . . . at . . . hours.
QUH   The current sea level barometric pressure is . . .
QUI   My navigation lights are working.
QUJ   The true track to reach me is . . . degrees.
QUK   The sea state at . . . is . . .
QUL   The sea swell at . . . is . . .
QUM   Normal working may be resumed.
QUN   My position, true course and speed are . . .

Notes
Codes QUO to QUZ are for search and rescue operations. Q codes can be given in the form of a question, when followed by a question mark. For example: QSJ? means 'what is the charge to be collected?'

HIGH-LEVEL DATA LINK CONTROL
FRAME STRUCTURE (ISO 3309)

In HDLC, all transmissions are in frames, and each frame conforms to the following format:

Flag	Address	Control	Information	FCS	Flag
01111110	8 bits	8 bits	*	16 bits	01111110

* An unspecified number of bits which in some cases may be a multiple of a particular character size, for example an octet.

where:
    Flag = flag sequence
    Address = station address field

Control = control field
Information = information field
FCS = frame checking sequence

Frames containing only supervisory control sequences form a special case where there is no information field. The format for these frames shall be:

Flag	Address	Control	FCS	Flag
01111110	8 bits	8 bits	16 bits	01111110

ISO OSI REFERENCE MODEL

END-USER
APPLICATION
PROCESS

FUNCTION

SELECTS APPROPRIATE SERVICE FOR APPLICATION	APPLICATION
PROVIDES CODE CONVERSION, DATA REFORMATTING	PRESENTATION
COORDINATES INTERACTION BETWEEN END-APPLICATION PROCESSES	SESSION
PROVIDES FOR END-TO-END DATA INTEGRITY AND QUALITY OF SERVICE	TRANSPORT
SWITCHES AND ROUTES INFORMATION	NETWORK
TRANSFERS UNIT OF INFORMATION TO OTHER END OF PHYSICAL LINK	DATA LINK
TRANSMITS BIT STREAM TO MEDIUM	PHYSICAL

ICAO COUNTRY CODES

AA	Australia	AG	Solomon Islands
AB	Australia (Queensland)	AH	Australia (Western Australia)
AC	Australia (Cocos and Christmas Islands)	AL	Australia (Tasmania)
		AM	Australia (Victoria-Tasmania)
AD	Australia (Northern Territory)		

AN	Nauru	GB	Gambia
AP	Australia (Western Australia)	GC	Canary Islands
AS	Australia (Capital Territory)	GE	Melilla
AT	Australia (Queensland)	GF	Sierra Leone
AY	Papua New Guinea	GL	Liberia
BG	Greenland	GM	Morocco
BI	Iceland	GO	Senegal
CF	Saint Pierre and Miquelon	GP	Guinea-Bissau
CU-CZ	Canada	GQ	Mauritania
DA	Algeria	GS	West Sahara
DD	Benin	GU	Guinea
DG	Ghana	GV	Cape Verde
DH	Upper Volta	HA	Ethiopia
DI	Ivory Coast	HC	Somalia
DN	Nigeria	HE	Egypt
DR	Niger	HF	Djibuti
DT	Tunisia	HK	Kenya
DX	Togo	HL	Libya
EB	Belgium	HS	Sudan
ED	Federal Republic of Germany	HT	Tanzania
EF	Finland	HU	Uganda
EG	United Kingdom	KA-KZ	U.S.A.
EH	Netherlands	LB	Bulgaria
EI	Eire	LC	Cyprus
EK	Denmark	LE	Spain
EL	Luxembourg	LF	France
EN	Norway	LG	Greece
EP	Poland	LH	Hungary
ES	Sweden	LI	Italy
ET	German Democratic Republic	LK	Czechoslavakia
FA	Republic of South Africa	LL	Israel
FB	Botswana	LM	Malta
FC	Congo	LO	Austria
FD	Swaziland	LP	Portugal
FE	Rwanda	LR	Romania
FF	Central African Republic	LS	Switzerland
FG	Equatorial Guinea	LT	Turkey
FH	Ascension Island	LX	Gibraltar
FI	Mauritius	LY	Yugoslavia
FJ	British Indian Ocean Territory	MA	Netherlands Antilles
FK	Cameroon	MB	Panama Canal Zone
FL	Zambia	MC	Colombia
FM	Comoro Islands	MD	Dominican Republic
FM	Réunion/Madagascar	ME	Surinam
FN	Angola	MF	French Antilles
FO	Gabon	MG	Guatemala
FP	São Tomé and Principe	MH	Honduras
FQ	Mozambique	MI	U.S. Virgin Islands
FR	Zimbabwe	MJ	Puerto Rico
FS	Seychelles	MK	Barbados
FT	Chad	MK	Cayman Islands
FU	Burundi	MK	Grenada
FW	Malawi	MK	Jamaica
FX	Lesotho	MK	Trinidad and Tobago
FZ	Zaire	MK	Turks & Caicos Islands
GA	Mali	MK	British Virgin Islands

ML	Guyana	PH	Hawaii
MM	Mexico	PJ	Johnston Island
MN	Nicaragua	PK	Marshall Islands
MO	French Guiana	PL	Line Islands
MP	Panama	PM	Midway Island
MR	Costa Rica	PT	Caroline Islands
MS	El Salvador	PW	Wake Island
MT	Haiti	RC	Taiwan
MU	Cuba	RJ	Japan
MV	Venezuela	RK	Korea
MX	Bermuda	RO	Japan
MY	Bahamas	RP	Philippines
MZ	Belize	SA	Argentina
NC	Cook Islands	SB	Brazil
NE	Easter Island	SC	Chile
NF	Fiji	SE	Equador
NF	Tonga	SF	Falkland Islands
NG	Gilbert Islands/Tuvalu	SG	Paraguay
NH	New Hebrides	SL	Bolivia
NI	Niue Island	SP	Peru
NL	Wallis and Futuna Islands	SU	Uruguay
NS	Western Samoa	UA–UY	U.S.S.R.
NS	American Samoa	VA	India
NT	French Polynesia	VB	Burma
NW	New Caledonia	VC	Sri Lanka
NZ	New Zealand	VD	Khmer Republic
OA	Afghanistan	VE	India
OB	Bahrain	VG	Bangladesh
OD	S. Yemen	VH	Hong Kong
OE	Saudi Arabia	VI	India
OI	Iran	VL	Laos
OJ	Jordan	VM	Macao
OK	Kuwait	VN	Nepal
OL	Lebanon	VO	India
OM	United Arab Emirates	VR	Maldive Islands
OO	Oman	VT	Thailand
OP	Pakistan	WA	Indonesia
OR	Iraq	WB	Brunei
OS	Syria	WB	Malaysia
OT	Qatar	WI	Indonesia
OY	N. Yemen	WM	Malaysia
PA	Alaska	WP	Timor
PB	Baker Island	WR	Indonesia
PC	Phoenix Islands	WS	Singapore
PG	Mariana Island	ZB–ZY	China (People's Republic)

8-BIT MICROPROCESSOR INSTRUCTION SET (ASM 8)

The tables below present ASM 8 instruction statements (for popular 8-bit microprocessors such as the Z80) as combinations of mnemonics and operands. A mnemonic is a symbolic representation of an instruction and the operand(s) are its required parameters.

For descriptions of the instruction bit patterns the reader is referred to manufacturer's manuals.

OPERAND TYPE SYMBOLS

Symbol	Operand type
numb	any numeric expression
acc	accumulator register
reg	any general purpose register
mem	any ADDRESS expression, with or without base and/or index-addressing modes
label	any ADDRESS expression which evaluates to a label
PC	Program counter

DATA TRANSFER INSTRUCTIONS

Syntax		Result
EX	DE, HL	exchange contents of DE & HL registers
EXX		exchange contents of BC, DE, & HL registers with corresponding alternates
IN	acc, mem	transfer data from input port given by mem to accumulator
IN	reg, mem	transfer data from input port given by mem to register
INI		transfer data from input port given by (C) to location specified by (HL) and increment counter
LD	reg, reg	transfer data from register to register
LD	acc, reg	transfer data from register to accumulator
LD	reg, acc	transfer data from accumulator to register
LD	mem, reg	transfer data from register to memory
LD	reg, mem	transfer data from memory to register
LDI		transfer data from memory location specified in HL to memory location specified in DE and increment pointers
LDD		as LDI but decrement pointers
LDIR		as LDI until BC = 0
LDDR		as LDD until BC = 0
OUT	mem, acc	transfer data to port specified by mem from accumulator
OUTI		transfer data to port specified by (C) from location specified by (HL) and increment pointer
POP	reg	pop contents of stack to register
PUSH	reg	push contents of register to stack

ARITHMETIC INSTRUCTIONS

ADD	acc, reg	contents of register added to accumulator
ADD	acc, n	add number n to accumulator
ADD	reg, reg	contents of register added to register
ADD	acc, mem	add memory to accumulator
ADC	acc, reg	contents of register added to accumulator with carry
ADC	acc, n	add number n to accumulator with carry
ADC	acc, mem	add memory to accumulator with carry

DAA		decimal adjust accumulator
DEC	reg	decrement contents of register
DEC	mem	decrement contents of memory
INC	reg	increment contents of register
SBC	acc, mem	subtract memory from accumulator with carry
SBC	acc, reg	subtract with carry register from accumulator
SBC	acc, n	subtract number n from accumulator with carry
SUB	acc, reg	subtract register from accumulator
SUB	acc, n	subtract number n from accumulator
SUB	mem	subtract memory from accumulator

LOGIC INSTRUCTIONS

AND	reg	logically and bit content of register with accumulator
AND	n	logically and n with accumulator
BIT	b, reg	test bit b in register
BIT	b, mem	test bit b in memory
CPL		complement accumulator
NEG		negate accumulator (2's complement)
OR	reg	logically or bit content of register with accumulator
OR	n	logically or n with accumulator
RES	b, reg	reset bit b in register
RES	b, mem	reset bit b in memory
SET	b, reg	set bit b in register
SET	b, mem	set bit b in memory
XOR	reg	exclusive or bit contents of register with accumulator
XOR	n	exclusive or n with accumulator

SHIFT INSTRUCTIONS

RL	reg	rotate register left through carry
RL	mem	rotate memory left through carry
RLC	reg	rotate register left circular
RLC	mem	rotate memory left circular
RLD		rotate digit left and right between accumulator and (HL)
RR	reg	rotate register right through carry
RR	mem	rotate memory right through carry
RRC	reg	rotate register right circular
RRC	mem	rotate memory right circular
RRD		rotate digit right and left between accumulator and (HL)
SLA	reg	shift register left arithmetic
SLA	mem	shift memory left arithmetic
SRA	reg	shift register right arithmetic
SRA	mem	shift memory right arithmetic
SRL	reg	shift register right logical
SRL	mem	shift memory right logical

PROGRAM CONTROL INSTRUCTIONS

CALL	mem	unconditional call to subroutine in location memory
CALL	C, mem	conditional call to subroutine (if C is true) in location memory
DJNZ	d	decrement register B and, if zero, jump to PC + d
JP	mem	unconditional jump
JP	(reg)	unconditional jump via register
JP	C, mem	conditional jump (if C is true)
JR	d	unconditional jump PC + d
JR	C, d	conditional jump to PC + d (if C is true)
RET		unconditional return from subroutine
RET	C	conditional return from subroutine (if C is true)
RETI		return from interrupt
RETN		return from non-maskable interrupt

PROCESSOR CONTROL INSTRUCTIONS

CCF		complement carry flag
DI		disable interrupts
EI		enable interrupts
HALT		halt processor
IM0		set interrupt mode 0
IM1		set interrupt mode 1
IM2		set interrupt mode 2
NOP		no operation
RST	mem	interrupt to location memory
SCF		set carry flag

COMPARISON INSTRUCTIONS

CP	reg	compare register contents with accumulator
CP	n	compare number n with accumulator
CP	mem	compare memory with accumulator
CPD		compare memory location (HL) with accumulator and decrement memory pointer and BC
CPI		compare memory location (HL) with accumulator and increment memory pointer and BC
CPDR		compare memory location (HL) with accumulator, decrement memory pointer and BC and repeat until (HL) = acc or BC = 0.

16-BIT MICROPROCESSOR INSTRUCTION SET (ASM 86–CP/M)

The table below presents ASM 86 instruction statements (for popular 16-bit microprocessor such as the 8086) as combinations of mnemonic and operands.

For descriptions of the instruction bit patterns the reader is referred to manufacturer's manuals.

OPERAND TYPE SYMBOLS

Symbol	Operand type
numb	any numeric expression
numb8	any numeric expression which evaluates to an 8-bit number
acc	accumulator register, AX or AL
reg	any general purpose register, not segment register
reg16	a 16-bit general purpose register, not segment register
segreg	any segment register: CS, DS, SS, or ES
mem	any ADDRESS expression, with or without base- and/or index-addressing modes, such as:

> variable
> variable+3
> variable[bx]
> variable[SI]
> variable[BX+SI]
> [BX]
> [BP+DI]

simpmem	any ADDRESS expression WITHOUT base- and index-addressing modes, such as:

> variable
> variable+4

mem|reg	any expression symbolised by 'reg' or 'mem'
mem|reg16	any expression symbolised by 'mem|reg', but must be 16 bits
label	any ADDRESS expression which evaluates to a label
lab8	any 'label' which is within +/− 128 bytes distance from the instruction

FLAG REGISTER SYMBOLS

AF	Auxiliary-Carry-Flag
CF	Carry-Flag
DF	Direction-Flag
IF	Interrupt-Enable-Flag
OF	Overflow-Flag
PF	Parity-Flag
SF	Sign-Flag
TF	Trap-Flag
ZF	Zero-Flag

DATA TRANSFER INSTRUCTIONS

Syntax		Result
IN	acc,numb8|numb16	transfer data from input port given by numb8 or numb16 (0–255) to accumulator
IN	acc,DX	transfer data from input port given by DX register (0–0FFFFH) to accumulator

LAHF		transfer SF, ZF, AF, PF, and CF flags to the AH register
LDS	reg16,mem	transfer the segment part of the memory address (DWORD variable) to the DS segment register, transfer the offset part to a general purpose 16-bit register
LEA	reg16,mem	transfer the offset of the memory address to a (16-bit) register
LES	reg16,mem	transfer the segment part of the memory address to the ES segment register, transfer the offset part to a 16-bit general purpose register
MOV	reg,mem|reg	move memory or register to register
MOV	mem|reg,reg	move register to memory or register
MOV	mem|reg,numb	move immediate data to memory or register
MOV	segreg,mem|reg16	move memory or register to segment register
MOV	mem|reg16,segreg	move segment register to memory or register
OUT	numb8|numb16,acc	transfer data from accumulator to output port (0–255) given by numb8 or numb16
OUT	DX,acc	transfer data from accumulator to output port (0–0FFFFH) given by DX register
POP	mem|reg16	move top stack element to memory or register
POP	segreg	move top stack element to segment register; note that CS segment register not allowed
POPF		transfer top stack element to flags
PUSH	mem|reg16	move memory or register to top stack element
PUSH	segreg	move segment register to top stack element
PUSHF		transfer flags to top stack element
SAHF		transfer the AH register to flags
XCHG	reg,mem|reg	exchange register and memory or register
XCHG	mem|reg,reg	exchange memory or register and register
XLAT	mem|reg	perform table lookup translation, table given by 'mem|reg', which is always BX. Replaces AL with AL offset from BX.

ARITHMETIC INSTRUCTIONS

Syntax	Result
AAA	adjust unpacked BCD (ASCII) for addition – adjusts AL
AAD	adjust unpacked BCD (ASCII) for division – adjusts AL
AAM	adjust unpacked BCD (ASCII) for multiplication – adjusts AX
AAS	adjust unpacked BCD (ASCII) for subtraction – adjusts AL

ADC	reg,mem|reg	add (with carry) memory or register to register
ADC	mem|reg,reg	add (with carry) register to memory or register
ADC	mem|reg,numb	add (with carry) immediate data to memory or register
ADD	reg,mem|reg	add memory or register to register
ADD	mem|reg,reg	add register to memory or register
ADD	mem|reg,numb	add immediate data to memory or register
CBW		convert byte in AL to word in AH by sign extension
CWD		convert word in AX to double word in DX/AX by sign extension
CMP	reg,mem|reg	compare register with memory or register
CMP	mem|reg,reg	compare memory or register with register
CMP	mem|reg,numb	compare data constant with memory or register
DAA		decimal adjust for addition, adjusts AL
DAS		decimal adjust for subtraction, adjusts AL
DEC	mem|reg	subtract 1 from memory or register
INC	mem|reg	add 1 to memory or register
DIV	mem|reg	divide (unsigned) accumulator (AX or AL) by memory or register. If byte results, AL = quotient, AH = remainder. If word results, AX = quotient, DX = remainder
IDIV	mem|reg	divide (signed) accumulator (AX or AL) by memory or register – quotient and remainder stored as in DIV
IMUL	mem|reg	multiply (signed) memory or register by accumulator (AX or AL) – if byte, results in AH, AL. If word, results in DX, AX
MUL	mem|reg	multiply (unsigned) memory or register by accumulator (AX or AL) – results stored as in IMUL
NEG	mem|reg	two's complement memory or register
SBB	reg,mem|reg	subtract (with borrow) memory or register from register
SBB	mem|reg,reg	subtract (with borrow) register from memory or register
SBB	mem|reg,numb	subtract (with borrow) immediate data from memory or register
SUB	reg,mem|reg	subtract memory or register from register
SUB	mem|reg,reg	subtract register from memory or register
SUB	mem|reg,numb	subtract data constant from memory or register

EFFECTS OF ARITHMETIC INSTRUCTIONS ON FLAGS

CF   is set if the operation resulted in a carry out of (from addition) or a borrow into (from subtraction) the high-order bit of the result; otherwise CF is cleared.

AF   is set if the operation resulted in a carry out of (from addition) or a borrow into (from subtraction) the low-order four bits of the result; otherwise AF is cleared.

ZF   is set if the result of the operation is zero; otherwise ZF is cleared.

SF   is set if the result is negative.

PF   is set if the modulo 2 sum of the low-order eight bits of the result of the operation is 0 (even parity); otherwise PF is cleared (odd parity).

OF   is set if the operation resulted in an overflow; the size of the result exceeded the capacity of its destination.

LOGIC AND SHIFT INSTRUCTIONS

Syntax		Result
AND	reg,mem|reg	perform bitwise logical and of a register and memory register
AND	mem|reg,reg	perform bitwise logical and of memory register and register
AND	mem|reg,numb	preform bitwise logical and of memory register and data constant
NOT	mem|reg	form one's complement of memory or register
OR	reg,mem|reg	perform bitwise logical or of a register and memory register
OR	mem|reg,reg	perform bitwise logical or of memory register and register
OR	mem|reg,numb	perform bitwise logical or of memory register and data constant
RCL	mem|reg,1	rotate memory or register 1 bit left through carry flag
RCL	mem|reg,CL	rotate memory or register left through carry flag, number of bits given by CL register
RCR	mem|reg,1	rotate memory or register 1 bit right through carry flag
RCR	mem|reg,CL	rotate memory or register right through carry flag, number of bits given by CL register
ROL	mem|reg,1	rotate memory or register 1 bit left
ROL	mem|reg,CL	rotate memory or register left, number of bits given by CL register
ROR	mem|reg,1	rotate memory or register 1 bit right
ROR	mem|reg,CL	rotate memory or register right, number of bits given by CL register
SAL	mem|reg,1	shift memory or register 1 bit left, shift in low-order zero bits

SAL	mem|reg,CL	shift memory or register left, number of bits given by CL register, shift in low-order zero bits
SAR	mem|reg,1	shift memory or register 1 bit right, shift in high-order bits equal to the original high-order bit
SAR	mem|reg,CL	shift memory or register right, number of bits given by CL register, shift in high-order bits equal to the original high-order bit
SHL	mem|reg,1	shift memory or register 1 bit left, shift in low-order zero bits – note that SHL is a different mnemonic for SAL
SHL	mem|reg,CL	shift memory or register left, number of bits given by CL register, shift in low-order zero bits – note that SHL is a different mnemonic for SAL
SHR	mem|reg,1	shift memory or register 1 bit right, shift in high-order zero bits
SHR	mem|reg,CL	shift memory or register right, number of bits given by CL register, shift in high-order zero bits
TEST	reg,mem|reg	perform bitwise logical and of a register and memory or register – set condition flags but do not change destination
TEST	mem|reg,reg	perform bitwise logical and of memory register and register – set condition flags but do not change destination
TEST	mem|reg,numb	perform bitwise logical and – test of memory register and data constant – set condition flags but do not change destination
XOR	reg,mem|reg	perform bitwise logical exclusive OR of register and memory or register
XOR	mem|reg,reg	perform bitwise logical exclusive OR of memory register and register
XOR	mem|reg,numb	perform bitwise logical exclusive OR of memory register and data constant

STRING INSTRUCTIONS

Syntax		Result
CMPS	mem|reg,mem|reg	subtract source from destination, affect flags, but do not return result
LODS	mem|reg	transfer a byte or word from the source operand to the accumulator
MOVS	mem|reg,mem|reg	move 1 byte (or word) from source to destination
SCAS	mem|reg	subtract destination operand from accumulator (AX or AL), affect flags, but do not return result

| STOS | mem\|reg | transfer a byte or word from accumulator to the destination operand |

PREFIX INSTRUCTIONS

Syntax	Result
REP	repeat until CX register is zero
REPZ	repeat until CX register is zero and zero flag (ZF) is not zero
REPE	equal to 'REPZ'
REPNZ	repeat until CX register is zero and zero flag (ZF) is zero
REPNE	equal to 'REPNZ'

CONTROL TRANSFER INSTRUCTIONS

Syntax		Result
CALL	label	push the offset address of the next instruction on the stack, jump to the target label
CALL	mem|reg16	push the offset address to the next instruction on the stack, jump to location indicated by contents of specified memory or register
CALLF	label	push CS segment register on the stack, push the offset address of the next instruction on the stack (after CS), jump to the target label
CALLF	mem	push CS register on the stack, push the offset address of the next instruction on the stack, jump to location indicated by contents of specified double word in memory
INT	numb8	push the flag registers (as in PUSHF), clear TF and IF flags, transfer control with an indirect call through any one of the 256 interrupt-vector elements – uses three levels of stack
INTO		if OF (the overflow flag) is set, push the flag registers (as in PUSHF), clear TF and IF flags, transfer control with an indirect call through interrupt-vector element 4 (location 10H) – if the OF flag is cleared, no operation takes place
IRET		transfer control to the return address saved by a previous interrupt operation, restore saved flag registers, as well as CS and IP – pops three levels of stack
JA	lab8	jump if 'not below or equal' or 'above' ((CF or ZF) = 0)

JAE	lab8	jump if 'not below' or 'above or equal' (CF = 0)
JB	lab8	jump if 'below' or 'not above or equal' (CF = 1)
JBE	lab8	jump if 'below or equal' or 'not above' ((CF or ZF) = 1)
JC	lab8	same as 'JB'
JCXZ	lab8	jump to target label if CX register is zero
JE	lab8	jump if 'equal' or 'zero' (ZF = 1)
JG	lab8	jump if 'not less or equal' or 'greater' (((SF xor OF) or ZF) = 0)
JGE	lab8	jump if 'not less' or 'greater or equal' ((SF xor OF) =0)
JL	lab8	jump if 'less' or 'not greater or equal' ((SF xor OF) = 1)
JLE	lab8	jump if 'less or equal' or 'not greater' (((SF xor OF) or ZF) = 1)
JMP	label	jump to the target label
JMP	mem|reg16	jump to location indicated by contents of specified memory or register
JMPF	label	jump to the target label possibly in another code segment
JMPS	lab8	jump to the target label within +/− 128 bytes from instruction
JNA	lab8	same as 'JBE'
JNAE	lab8	same as 'JB'
JNB	lab8	same as 'JAE'
JNBE	lab8	same as 'JA'
JNC	lab8	same as 'JNB'
JNE	lab8	jump if 'not equal' or 'not zero' (ZF = 0)
JNG	lab8	same as 'JLE'
JNGE	lab8	same as 'JL'
JNL	lab8	same as 'JGE'
JNLE	lab8	same as 'JG'
JNO	lab8	jump if 'not overflow' (OF = 0)
JNP	lab8	jump if 'not parity' or 'parity odd'
JNS	lab8	jump if 'not sign'
JNZ	lab8	same as 'JNE'
JO	lab8	jump if 'overflow' (OF = 1)
JP	lab8	jump if 'parity' or 'parity even' (PF = 1)
JPE	lab8	same as 'JP'
JPO	lab8	same as 'JNP'
JS	lab8	jump if 'sign' (SF = 1)
JZ	lab8	same as 'JE'
LOOP	lab8	decrement CX register by one, jump to target label if CX is not zero
LOOPE	lab8	decrement CX register by one, jump to target label if CX is not zero and the ZF flag is set – 'loop while zero' or 'loop while equal'

LOOPNE	lab8	decrement CX register by one, jump to target label if CX is not zero and ZF flag is cleared – 'loop while not zero' or 'loop while not equal'
LOOPNZ	lab8	same as 'LOOPNE'
LOOPZ	lab8	same as 'LOOPE'
RET		return to the return address pushed by a previous CALL instruction, increment stack pointer by 2
RET	numb	return to the address pushed by a previous CALL, increment stack pointer by 2+numb
RETF		return to the address pushed by a previous CALLF instruction, increment stack pointer by 4
RETF	numb	return to the address pushed by a previous CALLF instruction, increment stack pointer by 4+numb

PROCESSOR CONTROL INSTRUCTIONS

Syntax		Result
CLC		clear CF flag
CLD		clear DF flag, causing string instructions to auto-increment the operand pointers
CLI		clear IF flag, disabling maskable external interrupts
CMC		complement CF flag
ESC	numb8,mem|reg	do no operation other than compute the effective address and place it on the address bus (ESC is used by the 8087 numeric co-processor), 'numb8' must be in the range 0 to 63
LOCK		PREFIX instruction, causes the processor to assert the 'bus-lock' signal for the duration of the operation caused by the following instruction – the LOCK prefix instruction may precede any other instruction – buslock prevents co-processors from gaining the bus; this is useful for shared-resource semaphores
HLT		causes the processor to enter halt state until an interrupt is recognised
STC		set CF flag
STD		set DF flag, causing string instructions to auto-decrement the operand pointers
STI		set IF flag, enabling maskable external interrupts
WAIT		causes the processor to enter a 'wait' state if the signal on its 'TEST' pin is not asserted

3 Components

RESISTOR COLOUR CODES

FOUR BAND RESISTORS

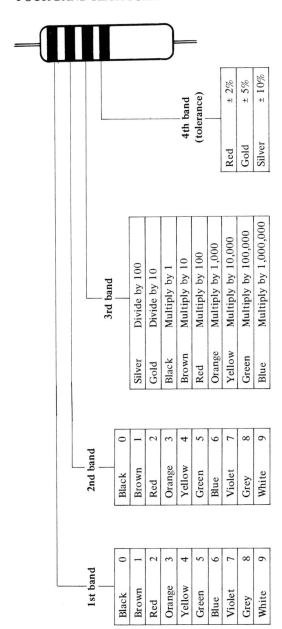

1st band

Black	0
Brown	1
Red	2
Orange	3
Yellow	4
Green	5
Blue	6
Violet	7
Grey	8
White	9

2nd band

Black	0
Brown	1
Red	2
Orange	3
Yellow	4
Green	5
Blue	6
Violet	7
Grey	8
White	9

3rd band

Silver	Divide by 100
Gold	Divide by 10
Black	Multiply by 1
Brown	Multiply by 10
Red	Multiply by 100
Orange	Multiply by 1,000
Yellow	Multiply by 10,000
Green	Multiply by 100,000
Blue	Multiply by 1,000,000

4th band (tolerance)

Red	± 2%
Gold	± 5%
Silver	± 10%

FIVE BAND RESISTORS

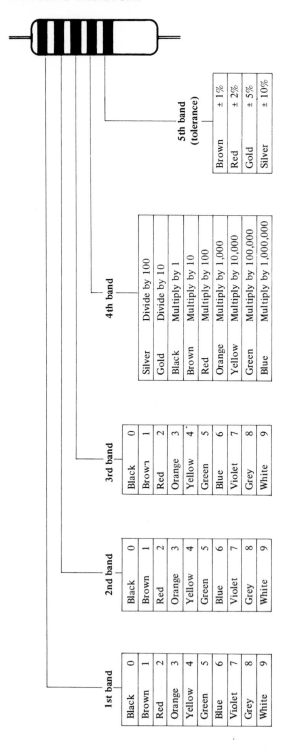

1st band

Black	0
Brown	1
Red	2
Orange	3
Yellow	4
Green	5
Blue	6
Violet	7
Grey	8
White	9

2nd band

Black	0
Brown	1
Red	2
Orange	3
Yellow	4
Green	5
Blue	6
Violet	7
Grey	8
White	9

3rd band

Black	0
Brown	1
Red	2
Orange	3
Yellow	4
Green	5
Blue	6
Violet	7
Grey	8
White	9

4th band

Silver	Divide by 100
Gold	Divide by 10
Black	Multiply by 1
Brown	Multiply by 10
Red	Multiply by 100
Orange	Multiply by 1,000
Yellow	Multiply by 10,000
Green	Multiply by 100,000
Blue	Multiply by 1,000,000

5th band (tolerance)

Brown	± 1%
Red	± 2%
Gold	± 5%
Silver	± 10%

SIX BAND RESISTORS

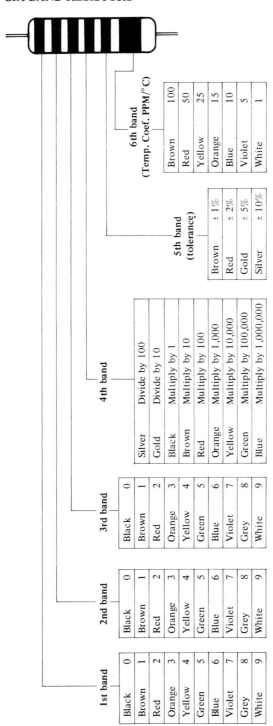

1st band

Black	0
Brown	1
Red	2
Orange	3
Yellow	4
Green	5
Blue	6
Violet	7
Grey	8
White	9

2nd band

Black	0
Brown	1
Red	2
Orange	3
Yellow	4
Green	5
Blue	6
Violet	7
Grey	8
White	9

3rd band

Black	0
Brown	1
Red	2
Orange	3
Yellow	4
Green	5
Blue	6
Violet	7
Grey	8
White	9

4th band

Silver	Divide by 100
Gold	Divide by 10
Black	Multiply by 1
Brown	Multiply by 10
Red	Multiply by 100
Orange	Multiply by 1,000
Yellow	Multiply by 10,000
Green	Multiply by 100,000
Blue	Multiply by 1,000,000

5th band (tolerance)

Brown	± 1%
Red	± 2%
Gold	± 5%
Silver	± 10%

6th band (Temp. Coef. PPM/°C)

Brown	100
Red	50
Yellow	25
Orange	15
Blue	10
Violet	5
White	1

CAPACITOR COLOUR CODES
POLYESTER CAPACITORS

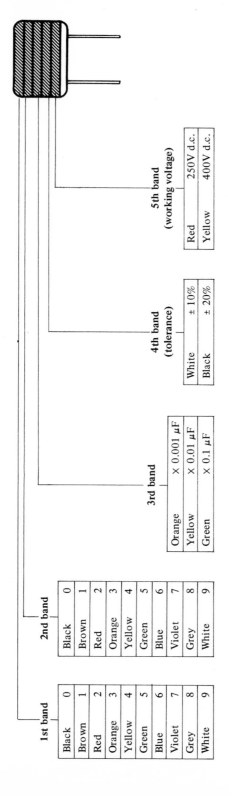

1st band

Black	0
Brown	1
Red	2
Orange	3
Yellow	4
Green	5
Blue	6
Violet	7
Grey	8
White	9

2nd band

Black	0
Brown	1
Red	2
Orange	3
Yellow	4
Green	5
Blue	6
Violet	7
Grey	8
White	9

3rd band

Orange	× 0.001 μF
Yellow	× 0.01 μF
Green	× 0.1 μF

4th band
(tolerance)

White	± 10%
Black	± 20%

5th band
(working voltage)

Red	250V d.c.
Yellow	400V d.c.

PREFERRED VALUES FOR RESISTORS AND CAPACITORS

Basic Values																								Series
10				15				22				33				47				68				E6
10		12		15		18		22		27		33		39		47		56		68		82		E12
10	11	12	13	15	16	18	20	22	24	27	30	33	36	39	43	47	51	56	62	68	75	82	91	E24

COMPARISON BETWEEN LOGIC IC TYPES

Type	Example	Features	Speed (MHz)	Supply voltage	Common applications
RTL (resistor-transistor logic)	Norbit	Early form of discrete logic	Slow	—	Mainly obsolete but still used in some slow automation applications
DTL (diode transistor logic)	800 Series	First type of integrated logic	$\simeq 1$	+3.6	Obsolete
TTL (transistor-transistor logic	74 Series	Development of DTL and is most popular logic family. Used for small (SSI) and medium (MSI) i.c.s.	10–40	+5(12)	Large range of standard circuit functions available
	74L	Low-power version	10	+5	Used where low current consumption or heat dissipation is needed
	74H	High-power/ speed	60	+5	—
Schottky TTL	74S	Faster than standard TTL. Schottky diodes used to prevent transistors from saturating	150	+5	Frequency counter prescalers. Synthesizers
ECL (emitter coupled logic)	10k Series 95 Series GH Series PECL	Non-saturating current mode logic (CML). Faster than TTL but lower logic level swing ($\simeq 1$V), therefore reduced noise immunity	250–1000	−5.2	Computer mainframes, prescalers for counters, frequency synthesizers. Also used for memories and programmable read-only memories
I^2L (integrated injection logic)	—	Bipolar logic. Very high density possible with low supply voltage. Linear circuits can be incorporated on same i.c.	—	—	At present used mainly for custom circuits

Type	Example	Features	Speed (MHz)	Supply voltage	Common applications
P-channel silicon gate	–	First type of m.o.s.f.e.t. logic. Low power consumption, easy to manufacture, high circuit density possible. Can be damaged by static	–	−10 to −20	Random access memories (RAM), Read-only memories (ROM), LSI devices, e.g. clock chips, microprocessors, etc.
Aluminium gate	–	Faster version of above	–	–	–
N-channel	–	M.o.s.f.e.t. logic compatible with TTL, slightly faster than P-channel	–	+5 to 20	As above
CMOS (complementary metal oxide silicon)	4000 Series MCMOS LOCMOS	Works over a wide range of supply voltages. Takes virtually no quiescent current (supply current is proportional to speed). Early types could be damaged by static, now incorporate protection diodes	5–10 (20 possible)	3–12	Large range of standard functions now available. Also MSI, LSI circuits. Can replace TTL in many circuits

'PRO-ELECTRON' NOMENCLATURE FOR SEMICONDUCTOR DEVICES

Transistors and similar devices are defined by two letters followed by a serial number (three figures or one letter and two figures). The serial number is manufacturer-dependent. The initial two letters define the device function as follows:

FIRST LETTER

Indicates the semiconductor material used:

A - Germanium
B - Silicon
C - Compound materials such as gallium arsenide
D - Compound materials such as indium antimonide
R - Compound materials such as cadmium sulphide

SECOND LETTER

Indicates the general device function:

A - Detection, high-speed or mixer diode

B - Variable capacitance diode

C - Transistor for AF (not power) applications

D - Transistor for AF power applications

E - Tunnel diode

F - Transistor for RF (not power) applications

G - Miscellaneous devices

L - Transistor for RF power applications

N - Photo-coupler

P - Radiation sensitive device (such as photo diode etc)

Q - Radiation generating device (such as light emitting diode)

R - Controlling or switching device (not power) such as thyristor

S - Transistor for switching (not power) applications

T - Controlling or switching power device

U - Transistor for power switching

X - Multiple diode (such as varactor)

Y - Rectifier, booster or efficiency diode

Z - Voltage reference, voltage regulator or transient suppressor diode

4 Numbers

POWERS OF 2

n	$2^{n\cdot}$	2^{-n}	$-n$
1	2	.5	−1
2	4	.25	−2
3	8	.125	−3
4	16	.062 5	−4
5	32	.031 25	−5
6	64	.015 625	−6
7	128	.007 812 5	−7
8	256	.003 906 25	−8
9	512	.001 953 125	−9
10	1 024	.000 976 562 5	−10
11	2 048	.000 488 281 25	−11
12	4 096	.000 244 140 625	−12
13	8 192	.000 122 070 312 5	−13
14	16 384	.000 061 035 156 25	−14
15	32 768	.000 030 517 578 125	−15
16	65 536	.000 015 258 789 062 5	−16
17	131 072	.000 007 629 394 531 25	−17
18	262 144	.000 003 814 679 265 625	−18
19	524 288	.000 001 907 348 632 812 5	−19
20	1 048 576	.000 000 953 674 316 406 25	−20
21	2 097 152	.000 000 476 837 158 203 125	−21
22	4 194 304	.000 000 238 418 579 101 562 5	−22
23	8 388 608	.000 000 119 209 289 550 781 25	−23
24	16 777 216	.000 000 059 604 644 775 390 625	−24
25	33 554 432	.000 000 029 802 322 387 695 312 5	−25
26	67 108 864	.000 000 014 901 161 193 847 656 25	−26
27	134 217 728	.000 000 007 450 580 596 923 828 125	−27
28	268 435 456	.000 000 003 725 290 298 461 914 062 5	−28
29	536 870 912	.000 000 001 862 645 149 230 957 031 25	−29
30	1 073 741 824	.000 000 000 931 322 574 615 478 515 625	−30
31	2 147 483 648	.000 000 000 465 661 287 307 739 257 812 5	−31
32	4 294 967 296	.000 000 000 232 830 643 653 869 628 906 25	−32

POWERS OF 10_{16}

10^n	n	10^{-n}				
1	0	1.0000	0000	0000	0000	
A	1	0.1999	9999	9999	999A	
64	2	0.28F5	C28F	5C28	F5C3	$\times\ 16^{-1}$
3E8	3	0.4189	374B	C6A7	EF9E	$\times\ 16^{-2}$
2710	4	0.68DB	8BAC	710C	B296	$\times\ 16^{-3}$
1 86A0	5	0.A7C5	AC47	1B47	8423	$\times\ 16^{-4}$
F 4240	6	0.10C6	F7A0	B5ED	8D37	$\times\ 16^{-4}$
98 9680	7	0.1AD7	F29A	BCAF	4858	$\times\ 16^{-5}$
5F5 E100	8	0.2AF3	1DC4	6118	73BF	$\times\ 16^{-6}$
3B9A CA00	9	0.44B8	2FA0	9B5A	52CC	$\times\ 16^{-7}$
2 540B E400	10	0.6DF3	7F67	5EF6	EADF	$\times\ 16^{-8}$
17 4876 E800	11	0.AFEB	FF0B	CB24	AAFF	$\times\ 16^{-9}$
E8 D4A5 1000	12	0.1197	9981	2DEA	1119	$\times\ 16^{-9}$
918 4E72 A000	13	0.1C25	C268	4976	81C2	$\times\ 16^{-10}$
5AF3 107A 4000	14	0.2D09	370D	4257	3604	$\times\ 16^{-11}$
3 8D7E A4C6 8000	15	0.480E	BE7B	9D58	566D	$\times\ 16^{-12}$
23 86F2 6FC1 0000	16	0.734A	CA5F	6226	F0AE	$\times\ 16^{-13}$
163 4578 5D8A 0000	17	0.B877	AA32	36A4	B449	$\times\ 16^{-14}$
DE0 B6B3 A764 0000	18	0.1272	5DD1	D243	ABA1	$\times\ 16^{-14}$
8AC7 2304 89E8 0000	19	0.1D83	C94F	B6D2	AC35	$\times\ 16^{-15}$

POWERS OF 16_{10}

16^n	n	16^{-n}				
1	0	0.10000	00000	00000	00000	$\times\ 10$
16	1	0.62500	00000	00000	00000	$\times\ 10^{-1}$
256	2	0.39062	50000	00000	00000	$\times\ 10^{-2}$
4 096	3	0.24414	06250	00000	00000	$\times\ 10^{-3}$
65 536	4	0.15258	78906	25000	00000	$\times\ 10^{-4}$
1 048 576	5	0.95367	43164	06250	00000	$\times\ 10^{-6}$
16 777 216	6	0.59604	64477	53906	25000	$\times\ 10^{-7}$
268 435 456	7	0.37252	90298	46191	40625	$\times\ 10^{-8}$
4 294 967 296	8	0.23283	06436	53869	62891	$\times\ 10^{-9}$
68 719 476 736	9	0.14551	91522	83668	51807	$\times\ 10^{-10}$
1 099 511 627 776	10	0.90949	47017	72928	23792	$\times\ 10^{-12}$
17 592 186 044 416	11	0.56843	41886	08080	14870	$\times\ 10^{-13}$
281 474 976 710 656	12	0.35527	13678	80050	09294	$\times\ 10^{-14}$
4 503 599 627 370 496	13	0.22204	46049	25031	30808	$\times\ 10^{-15}$
72 057 594 037 927 936	14	0.13877	78780	78144	56755	$\times\ 10^{-16}$
1 152 921 504 606 846 976	15	0.86736	17379	88403	54721	$\times\ 10^{-18}$

NUMBER CONVERSION, DECIMAL TO OCTAL AND VICE VERSA

DECIMAL TO OCTAL

Decimal numbers are listed sequentially in the main body. To convert to octal, locate the row (left hand 3 figures) and column (heading figure) corresponding to the required decimal value. The octal value is given by the 3 figures concatenated with the heading figure. For example, decimal 2439 is equivalent to octal 4607.

OCTAL TO DECIMAL

The four digit octal number (with leading zeros if necessary) is located by its leading three figures (giving the row) and fourth (right hand) figure giving the column. The intersection of this row and column is the equivalent decimal value. For example, octal 216 is equivalent to decimal 142.

	0	1	2	3	4	5	6	7
0410	0064	0065	0066	0067	0068	0069	0070	0071
0411	0072	0073	0074	0075	0076	0077	0078	0079
0412	0080	0081	0082	0083	0084	0085	0086	0087
0413	0088	0089	0090	0091	0092	0093	0094	0095
0414	0096	0097	0098	0099	0100	0101	0102	0103
0415	0104	0105	0106	0107	0108	0109	0110	0111
0416	0112	0113	0114	0115	0116	0117	0118	0119
0417	0120	0121	0122	0123	0124	0125	0126	0127

	0	1	2	3	4	5	6	7
0000	0000	0001	0002	0003	0004	0005	0006	0007
0001	0008	0009	0010	0011	0012	0013	0014	0015
0002	0016	0017	0018	0019	0020	0021	0022	0023
0003	0024	0025	0026	0027	0028	0029	0030	0031
0004	0032	0033	0034	0035	0036	0037	0038	0039
0005	0040	0041	0042	0043	0044	0045	0046	0047
0006	0048	0049	0050	0051	0052	0053	0054	0055
0007	0056	0057	0058	0059	0060	0061	0062	0063

	0	1	2	3	4	5	6	7
030	0192	0193	0194	0195	0196	0197	0198	0199
031	0200	0201	0202	0203	0204	0205	0206	0207
032	0208	0209	0210	0211	0212	0213	0214	0215
033	0216	0217	0218	0219	0220	0221	0222	0223
034	0224	0225	0226	0227	0228	0229	0230	0231
035	0232	0233	0234	0235	0236	0237	0238	0239
036	0240	0241	0242	0243	0244	0245	0246	0247
037	0248	0249	0250	0251	0252	0253	0254	0255

	0	1	2	3	4	5	6	7
020	0128	0129	0130	0131	0132	0133	0134	0135
021	0136	0137	0138	0139	0140	0141	0142	0143
022	0144	0145	0146	0147	0148	0149	0150	0151
023	0152	0153	0154	0155	0156	0157	0158	0159
024	0160	0161	0162	0163	0164	0165	0166	0167
025	0168	0169	0170	0171	0172	0173	0174	0175
026	0176	0177	0178	0179	0180	0181	0182	0183
027	0184	0185	0186	0187	0188	0189	0190	0191

	0	1	2	3	4	5	6	7
050	0320	0321	0322	0323	0324	0325	0326	0327
051	0328	0329	0330	0331	0332	0333	0334	0335
052	0336	0337	0338	0339	0340	0341	0342	0343
053	0344	0345	0346	0347	0348	0349	0350	0351
054	0352	0353	0354	0355	0356	0357	0358	0359
055	0360	0361	0362	0363	0364	0365	0366	0367
056	0368	0369	0370	0371	0372	0373	0374	0375
057	0376	0377	0378	0379	0380	0381	0382	0383

	0	1	2	3	4	5	6	7
040	0256	0257	0258	0259	0260	0261	0262	0263
041	0264	0265	0266	0267	0268	0269	0270	0271
042	0272	0273	0274	0275	0276	0277	0278	0279
043	0280	0281	0282	0283	0284	0285	0286	0287
044	0288	0289	0290	0291	0292	0293	0294	0295
045	0296	0297	0298	0299	0300	0301	0302	0303
046	0304	0305	0306	0307	0308	0309	0310	0311
047	0312	0313	0314	0315	0316	0317	0318	0319

	0	1	2	3	4	5	6	7
070	0448	0449	0450	0451	0452	0453	0454	0455
071	0456	0457	0458	0459	0460	0461	0462	0463
072	0464	0465	0466	0467	0468	0469	0470	0471
073	0472	0473	0474	0475	0476	0477	0478	0479
074	0480	0481	0482	0483	0484	0485	0486	0487
075	0488	0489	0490	0491	0492	0493	0494	0495
076	0496	0497	0498	0499	0500	0501	0502	0503
077	0504	0505	0506	0507	0508	0509	0510	0511

	0	1	2	3	4	5	6	7
060	0384	0385	0386	0387	0388	0389	0390	0391
061	0392	0393	0394	0395	0396	0397	0398	0399
062	0400	0401	0402	0403	0404	0405	0406	0407
063	0408	0409	0410	0411	0412	0413	0414	0415
064	0416	0417	0418	0419	0420	0421	0422	0423
065	0424	0425	0426	0427	0428	0429	0430	0431
066	0432	0433	0434	0435	0436	0437	0438	0439
067	0440	0441	0442	0443	0444	0445	0446	0447

	0	1	2	3	4	5	6	7
110	0576	0577	0578	0579	0580	0581	0582	0583
111	0584	0585	0586	0587	0588	0589	0590	0591
112	0592	0593	0594	0595	0596	0597	0598	0599
113	0600	0601	0602	0603	0604	0605	0606	0607
114	0608	0609	0610	0611	0612	0613	0614	0615
115	0616	0617	0618	0619	0620	0621	0622	0623
116	0624	0625	0626	0627	0628	0629	0630	0631
117	0632	0633	0634	0635	0636	0637	0638	0639

	0	1	2	3	4	5	6	7
100	0512	0513	0514	0515	0516	0517	0518	0519
101	0520	0521	0522	0523	0524	0525	0526	0527
102	0528	0529	0530	0531	0532	0533	0534	0535
103	0536	0537	0538	0539	0540	0541	0542	0543
104	0544	0545	0546	0547	0548	0549	0550	0551
105	0552	0553	0554	0555	0556	0557	0558	0559
106	0560	0561	0562	0563	0564	0565	0566	0567
107	0568	0569	0570	0571	0572	0573	0574	0575

	0	1	2	3	4	5	6	7
430	0704	0705	0706	0707	0708	0709	0710	0711
431	0712	0713	0714	0715	0716	0717	0718	0719
432	0720	0721	0722	0723	0724	0725	0726	0727
433	0728	0729	0730	0731	0732	0733	0734	0735
434	0736	0737	0738	0739	0740	0741	0742	0743
435	0744	0745	0746	0747	0748	0749	0750	0751
436	0752	0753	0754	0755	0756	0757	0758	0759
437	0760	0761	0762	0763	0764	0765	0766	0767

	0	1	2	3	4	5	6	7
420	0640	0641	0642	0643	0644	0645	0646	0647
421	0648	0649	0650	0651	0652	0653	0654	0655
422	0656	0657	0658	0659	0660	0661	0662	0663
423	0664	0665	0666	0667	0668	0669	0670	0671
424	0672	0673	0674	0675	0676	0677	0678	0679
425	0680	0681	0682	0683	0684	0685	0686	0687
426	0688	0689	0690	0691	0692	0693	0694	0695
427	0696	0697	0698	0699	0700	0701	0702	0703

7	6	5	4	3	2	1	0	
0839	0838	0837	0836	0835	0834	0833	0832	450
0847	0846	0845	0844	0843	0842	0841	0840	451
0855	0854	0853	0852	0851	0850	0849	0848	452
0863	0862	0861	0860	0859	0858	0857	0856	453
0871	0870	0869	0868	0867	0866	0865	0864	454
0879	0878	0877	0876	0875	0874	0873	0872	455
0887	0886	0885	0884	0883	0882	0881	0880	456
0895	0894	0893	0892	0891	0890	0889	0888	457

7	6	5	4	3	2	1	0	
0775	0774	0773	0772	0771	0770	0769	0768	440
0783	0782	0781	0780	0779	0778	0777	0776	441
0791	0790	0789	0788	0787	0786	0785	0784	442
0799	0798	0797	0796	0795	0794	0793	0792	443
0807	0806	0805	0804	0803	0802	0801	0800	444
0815	0814	0813	0812	0811	0810	0809	0808	445
0823	0822	0821	0820	0819	0818	0817	0816	446
0831	0830	0829	0828	0827	0826	0825	0824	447

	0	1	2	3	4	5	6	7
170	0960	0961	0962	0963	0964	0965	0966	0967
171	0968	0969	0970	0971	0972	0973	0974	0975
172	0976	0977	0978	0979	0980	0981	0982	0983
173	0984	0985	0986	0987	0988	0989	0990	0991
174	0992	0993	0994	0995	0996	0997	0998	0999
175	1000	1001	1002	1003	1004	1005	1006	1007
176	1008	1009	1010	1011	1012	1013	1014	1015
177	1016	1017	1018	1019	1020	1021	1022	1023

	0	1	2	3	4	5	6	7
160	0896	0897	0898	0899	0900	0901	0902	0903
161	0904	0905	0906	0907	0908	0909	0910	0911
162	0912	0913	0914	0915	0916	0917	0918	0919
163	0920	0921	0922	0923	0924	0925	0926	0927
164	0928	0929	0930	0931	0932	0933	0934	0935
165	0936	0937	0938	0939	0940	0941	0942	0943
166	0944	0945	0946	0947	0948	0949	0950	0951
167	0952	0953	0954	0955	0956	0957	0958	0959

	7	6	5	4	3	2	1	0
240	1095	1094	1093	1092	1091	1090	1089	1088
241	1103	1102	1101	1100	1099	1098	1097	1096
242	1111	1110	1109	1108	1107	1106	1105	1104
243	1119	1118	1117	1116	1115	1114	1113	1112
244	1127	1126	1125	1124	1123	1122	1121	1120
245	1135	1134	1133	1132	1131	1130	1129	1128
246	1143	1142	1141	1140	1139	1138	1137	1136
247	1151	1150	1149	1148	1147	1146	1145	1144

	7	6	5	4	3	2	1	0
200	1031	1030	1029	1028	1027	1026	1025	1024
201	1039	1038	1037	1036	1035	1034	1033	1032
202	1047	1046	1045	1044	1043	1042	1041	1040
203	1055	1054	1053	1052	1051	1050	1049	1048
204	1063	1062	1061	1060	1059	1058	1057	1056
205	1071	1070	1069	1068	1067	1066	1065	1064
206	1079	1078	1077	1076	1075	1074	1073	1072
207	1087	1086	1085	1084	1083	1082	1081	1080

	0	1	2	3	4	5	6	7
230	1216	1217	1218	1219	1220	1221	1222	1223
231	1224	1225	1226	1227	1228	1229	1230	1231
232	1232	1233	1234	1235	1236	1237	1238	1239
233	1240	1241	1242	1243	1244	1245	1246	1247
234	1248	1249	1250	1251	1252	1253	1254	1255
235	1256	1257	1258	1259	1260	1261	1262	1263
236	1264	1265	1266	1267	1268	1269	1270	1271
237	1272	1273	1274	1275	1276	1277	1278	1279

	0	1	2	3	4	5	6	7
220	1152	1153	1154	1155	1156	1157	1158	1159
221	1160	1161	1162	1163	1164	1165	1166	1167
222	1168	1169	1170	1171	1172	1173	1174	1175
223	1176	1177	1178	1179	1180	1181	1182	1183
224	1184	1185	1186	1187	1188	1189	1190	1191
225	1192	1193	1194	1195	1196	1197	1198	1199
226	1200	1201	1202	1203	1204	1205	1206	1207
227	1208	1209	1210	1211	1212	1213	1214	1215

	0	1	2	3	4	5	6	7
250	1344	1345	1346	1347	1348	1349	1350	1351
251	1352	1353	1354	1355	1356	1357	1358	1359
252	1360	1361	1362	1363	1364	1365	1366	1367
253	1368	1369	1370	1371	1372	1373	1374	1375
254	1376	1377	1378	1379	1380	1381	1382	1383
255	1384	1385	1386	1387	1388	1389	1390	1391
256	1392	1393	1394	1395	1396	1397	1398	1399
257	1400	1401	1402	1403	1404	1405	1406	1407

	0	1	2	3	4	5	6	7
240	1280	1281	1282	1283	1284	1285	1286	1287
241	1288	1289	1290	1291	1292	1293	1294	1295
242	1296	1297	1298	1299	1300	1301	1302	1303
243	1304	1305	1306	1307	1308	1309	1310	1311
244	1312	1313	1314	1315	1316	1317	1318	1319
245	1320	1321	1322	1323	1324	1325	1326	1327
246	1328	1329	1330	1331	1332	1333	1334	1335
247	1336	1337	1338	1339	1340	1341	1342	1343

	7	6	5	4	3	2	1	0
270	1479	1478	1477	1476	1475	1474	1473	1472
271	1487	1486	1485	1484	1483	1482	1481	1480
272	1495	1494	1493	1492	1491	1490	1489	1488
273	1503	1502	1501	1500	1499	1498	1497	1496
274	1511	1510	1509	1508	1507	1506	1505	1504
275	1519	1518	1517	1516	1515	1514	1513	1512
276	1527	1526	1525	1524	1523	1522	1521	1520
277	1535	1534	1533	1532	1531	1530	1529	1528

	7	6	5	4	3	2	1	0
260	1415	1414	1413	1412	1411	1410	1409	1408
261	1423	1422	1421	1420	1419	1418	1417	1416
262	1431	1430	1429	1428	1427	1426	1425	1424
263	1439	1438	1437	1436	1435	1434	1433	1432
264	1447	1446	1445	1444	1443	1442	1441	1440
265	1455	1454	1453	1452	1451	1450	1449	1448
266	1463	1462	1461	1460	1459	1458	1457	1456
267	1471	1470	1469	1468	1467	1466	1465	1464

	0	1	2	3	4	5	6	7
340	1600	1601	1602	1603	1604	1605	1606	1607
341	1608	1609	1610	1611	1612	1613	1614	1615
342	1616	1617	1618	1619	1620	1621	1622	1623
343	1624	1625	1626	1627	1628	1629	1630	1631
344	1632	1633	1634	1635	1636	1637	1638	1639
345	1640	1641	1642	1643	1644	1645	1646	1647
346	1648	1649	1650	1651	1652	1653	1654	1655
347	1656	1657	1658	1659	1660	1661	1662	1663

	0	1	2	3	4	5	6	7
300	1536	1537	1538	1539	1540	1541	1542	1543
301	1544	1545	1546	1547	1548	1549	1550	1551
302	1552	1553	1554	1555	1556	1557	1558	1559
303	1560	1561	1562	1563	1564	1565	1566	1567
304	1568	1569	1570	1571	1572	1573	1574	1575
305	1576	1577	1578	1579	1580	1581	1582	1583
306	1584	1585	1586	1587	1588	1589	1590	1591
307	1592	1593	1594	1595	1596	1597	1598	1599

	0	1	2	3	4	5	6	7
320	1664	1665	1666	1667	1668	1669	1670	1671
321	1672	1673	1674	1675	1676	1677	1678	1679
322	1680	1681	1682	1683	1684	1685	1686	1687
323	1688	1689	1690	1691	1692	1693	1694	1695
324	1696	1697	1698	1699	1700	1701	1702	1703
325	1704	1705	1706	1707	1708	1709	1710	1711
326	1712	1713	1714	1715	1716	1717	1718	1719
327	1720	1721	1722	1723	1724	1725	1726	1727

	0	1	2	3	4	5	6	7
330	1728	1729	1730	1731	1732	1733	1734	1735
331	1736	1737	1738	1739	1740	1741	1742	1743
332	1744	1745	1746	1747	1748	1749	1750	1751
333	1752	1753	1754	1755	1756	1757	1758	1759
334	1760	1761	1762	1763	1764	1765	1766	1767
335	1768	1769	1770	1771	1772	1773	1774	1775
336	1776	1777	1778	1779	1780	1781	1782	1783
337	1784	1785	1786	1787	1788	1789	1790	1791

7	6	5	4	3	2	1	0	
1863	1862	1861	1860	1859	1858	1857	1856	350
1871	1870	1869	1868	1867	1866	1865	1864	351
1879	1878	1877	1875	1875	1874	1873	1872	352
1887	1886	1885	1884	1883	1882	1881	1880	353
1895	1894	1893	1892	1891	1890	1889	1888	354
1903	1902	1901	1900	1899	1898	1897	1896	355
1911	1910	1909	1908	1907	1906	1905	1904	356
1919	1918	1917	1916	1915	1914	1913	1912	357

7	6	5	4	3	2	1	0	
1799	1798	1797	1796	1795	1794	1793	1792	340
1807	1806	1805	1804	1803	1802	1801	1800	341
1815	1814	1813	1812	1811	1810	1809	1808	342
1823	1822	1821	1820	1819	1818	1817	1816	343
1831	1830	1829	1828	1827	1826	1825	1824	344
1839	1838	1837	1836	1835	1834	1833	1832	345
1847	1846	1845	1844	1843	1842	1841	1840	346
1855	1854	1853	1852	1851	1850	1849	1848	347

	0	1	2	3	4	5	6	7
370	1984	1985	1986	1987	1988	1989	1990	1991
371	1992	1993	1994	1995	1996	1997	1998	1999
372	2000	2001	2002	2003	2004	2005	2006	2007
373	2008	2009	2010	2011	2012	2013	2014	2015
374	2016	2017	2018	2019	2020	2021	2022	2023
375	2024	2025	2026	2027	2028	2029	2030	2031
376	2032	2033	2034	2035	2036	2037	2038	2039
377	2040	2041	2042	2043	2044	2045	2046	2047

	0	1	2	3	4	5	6	7
360	1920	1921	1922	1923	1924	1925	1926	1927
361	1928	1929	1930	1931	1932	1933	1934	1935
362	1936	1937	1938	1939	1940	1941	1942	1943
363	1944	1945	1946	1947	1948	1949	1950	1951
364	1952	1953	1954	1955	1956	1957	1958	1959
365	1960	1961	1962	1963	1964	1965	1966	1967
366	1968	1969	1970	1971	1972	1973	1974	1975
367	1976	1977	1978	1979	1980	1981	1982	1983

	0	1	2	3	4	5	6	7
410	2412	2413	2414	2415	2416	2417	2418	2419
411	2420	2421	2422	2423	2424	2425	2426	2427
412	2428	2429	2430	2431	2432	2433	2434	2435
413	2436	2437	2438	2439	2440	2441	2442	2443
414	2444	2445	2446	2447	2448	2449	2450	2451
415	2452	2453	2454	2455	2456	2457	2458	2459
416	2460	2461	2462	2463	2464	2465	2466	2467
417	2468	2469	2470	2471	2472	2473	2474	2475

	0	1	2	3	4	5	6	7
400	2048	2049	2050	2051	2052	2053	2054	2055
401	2056	2057	2058	2059	2060	2061	2062	2063
402	2064	2065	2066	2067	2068	2069	2070	2071
403	2072	2073	2074	2075	2076	2077	2078	2079
404	2080	2081	2082	2083	2084	2085	2086	2087
405	2088	2089	2090	2091	2092	2093	2094	2095
406	2096	2097	2098	2099	2100	2101	2102	2103
407	2104	2105	2106	2107	2108	2109	2110	2111

	0	1	2	3	4	5	6	7
430	2240	2241	2242	2243	2244	2245	2246	2247
431	2248	2249	2250	2251	2252	2253	2254	2255
432	2256	2257	2258	2259	2260	2261	2262	2263
433	2264	2265	2266	2267	2268	2269	2270	2271
434	2272	2273	2274	2275	2276	2277	2278	2279
435	2280	2281	2282	2283	2284	2285	2286	2287
436	2288	2289	2290	2291	2292	2293	2294	2295
437	2296	2297	2298	2299	2300	2301	2302	2303

	0	1	2	3	4	5	6	7
420	2176	2177	2178	2179	2180	2181	2182	2183
421	2184	2185	2186	2187	2188	2189	2190	2191
422	2192	2193	2194	2195	2196	2197	2198	2199
423	2200	2201	2202	2203	2204	2205	2206	2207
424	2208	2209	2210	2211	2212	2213	2214	2215
425	2216	2217	2218	2219	2220	2221	2222	2223
426	2224	2225	2226	2227	2228	2229	2230	2231
427	2232	2233	2234	2235	2236	2237	2238	2239

	0	1	2	3	4	5	6	7
450	2368	2369	2370	2371	2372	2373	2374	2375
451	2376	2377	2378	2379	2380	2381	2382	2383
452	2384	2385	2386	2387	2388	2389	2390	2391
453	2392	2393	2394	2395	2396	2397	2398	2399
454	2400	2401	2402	2403	2404	2405	2406	2407
455	2408	2409	2410	2411	2412	2413	2414	2415
456	2416	2417	2418	2419	2420	2421	2422	2423
457	2424	2425	2426	2427	2428	2429	2430	2431

	0	1	2	3	4	5	6	7
440	2304	2305	2306	2307	2308	2309	2310	2311
441	2312	2313	2314	2315	2316	2317	2318	2319
442	2320	2321	2322	2323	2324	2325	2326	2327
443	2328	2329	2330	2331	2332	2333	2334	2335
444	2336	2337	2338	2339	2340	2341	2342	2343
445	2344	2345	2346	2347	2348	2349	2350	2351
446	2352	2353	2354	2355	2356	2357	2358	2359
447	2360	2361	2362	2363	2364	2365	2366	2367

	0	1	2	3	4	5	6	7
470	2496	2497	2498	2499	2500	2501	2502	2503
471	2504	2505	2506	2507	2508	2509	2510	2511
472	2512	2513	2514	2515	2516	2517	2518	2519
473	2520	2521	2522	2523	2524	2525	2526	2527
474	2528	2529	2530	2531	2532	2533	2534	2535
475	2536	2537	2538	2539	2540	2541	2542	2543
476	2544	2545	2546	2547	2548	2549	2550	2551
477	2552	2553	2554	2555	2556	2557	2558	2559

	0	1	2	3	4	5	6	7
460	2432	2433	2434	2435	2436	2437	2438	2439
461	2440	2441	2442	2443	2444	2445	2446	2447
462	2448	2449	2450	2451	2452	2453	2454	2455
463	2456	2457	2458	2459	2460	2461	2462	2463
464	2464	2465	2466	2467	2468	2469	2470	2471
465	2472	2473	2474	2475	2476	2477	2478	2479
466	2480	2481	2482	2483	2484	2485	2486	2487
467	2488	2489	2490	2491	2492	2493	2494	2495

	510	511	512	513	514	515	516	517
0	2624	2632	2640	2648	2656	2664	2672	2680
1	2625	2633	2641	2649	2657	2665	2673	2681
2	2626	2634	2642	2650	2658	2666	2674	2682
3	2627	2635	2643	2651	2659	2667	2675	2683
4	2628	2636	2644	2652	2660	2668	2676	2684
5	2629	2637	2645	2653	2661	2669	2677	2685
6	2630	2638	2646	2654	2662	2670	2678	2686
7	2631	2639	2647	2655	2663	2671	2679	2687

	500	501	502	503	504	505	506	507
0	2560	2568	2576	2584	2592	2600	2608	2616
1	2561	2569	2577	2585	2593	2601	2609	2617
2	2562	2570	2578	2586	2594	2602	2610	2618
3	2563	2571	2579	2587	2595	2603	2611	2619
4	2564	2572	2580	2588	2596	2604	2612	2620
5	2565	2573	2581	2589	2597	2605	2613	2621
6	2566	2574	2582	2590	2598	2606	2614	2622
7	2567	2575	2583	2591	2599	2607	2615	2623

	7	6	5	4	3	2	1	0
7	2759	2767	2775	2783	2791	2799	2807	2815
6	2758	2766	2774	2782	2790	2798	2806	2814
5	2757	2765	2773	2781	2789	2797	2805	2813
4	2756	2764	2772	2780	2788	2796	2804	2812
3	2755	2763	2771	2779	2787	2795	2803	2811
2	2754	2762	2770	2778	2786	2794	2802	2810
1	2753	2761	2769	2777	2785	2793	2801	2809
0	2752	2760	2768	2776	2784	2792	2800	2808
	530	531	532	533	534	535	536	537

	7	6	5	4	3	2	1	0
7	2695	2703	2711	2719	2727	2735	2743	2751
6	2694	2702	2710	2718	2726	2734	2742	2750
5	2693	2701	2709	2717	2725	2733	2741	2749
4	2692	2700	2708	2716	2724	2732	2740	2748
3	2691	2699	2707	2715	2723	2731	2739	2747
2	2690	2698	2706	2714	2722	2730	2738	2746
1	2689	2697	2705	2713	2721	2729	2737	2745
0	2688	2696	2704	2712	2720	2728	2736	2744
	520	521	522	523	524	525	526	527

	7	6	5	4	3	2	1	0
550	2887	2886	2885	2884	2883	2882	2881	2880
551	2895	2894	2893	2892	2891	2890	2889	2888
552	2903	2902	2901	2900	2899	2898	2897	2896
553	2911	2910	2909	2908	2907	2906	2905	2904
554	2919	2918	2917	2916	2915	2914	2913	2912
555	2927	2926	2925	2924	2923	2922	2921	2920
556	2935	2934	2933	2932	2931	2930	2929	2928
557	2943	2942	2941	2940	2939	2938	2937	2936

	7	6	5	4	3	2	1	0
540	2823	2822	2821	2820	2819	2818	2817	2816
541	2831	2830	2829	2828	2827	2826	2825	2824
542	2839	2838	2837	2836	2835	2834	2833	2832
543	2847	2846	2845	2844	2843	2842	2841	2840
544	2855	2854	2853	2852	2851	2850	2849	2848
545	2863	2862	2861	2860	2859	2858	2857	2856
546	2871	2870	2869	2868	2867	2866	2865	2864
547	2879	2878	2877	2876	2875	2874	2873	2872

	0	1	2	3	4	5	6	7
570	3008	3009	3010	3011	3012	3013	3014	3015
571	3016	3017	3018	3019	3020	3021	3022	3023
572	3024	3025	3026	3027	3028	3029	3030	3031
573	3032	3033	3034	3035	3036	3037	3038	3039
574	3040	3041	3042	3043	3044	3045	3046	3047
575	3048	3049	3050	3051	3052	3053	3054	3055
576	3056	3057	3058	3059	3060	3061	3062	3063
577	3064	3065	3066	3067	3068	3069	3070	3071

	0	1	2	3	4	5	6	7
560	2944	2945	2946	2947	2948	2949	2950	2951
561	2952	2953	2954	2955	2956	2957	2958	2959
562	2960	2961	2962	2963	2964	2965	2966	2967
563	2968	2969	2970	2971	2972	2973	2974	2975
564	2976	2977	2978	2979	2980	2981	2982	2983
565	2984	2985	2986	2987	2988	2989	2990	2991
566	2992	2993	2994	2995	2996	2997	2998	2999
567	3000	3001	3002	3003	3004	3005	3006	3007

	0	1	2	3	4	5	6	7
6400	3436	3437	3438	3439	3440	3441	3442	3443
6401	3444	3445	3446	3447	3448	3449	3450	3451
6402	3452	3453	3454	3455	3456	3457	3458	3459
6403	3460	3461	3462	3463	3464	3465	3466	3467
6404	3468	3469	3470	3471	3472	3473	3474	3475
6405	3476	3477	3478	3479	3480	3481	3482	3483
6406	3484	3485	3486	3487	3488	3489	3490	3491
6407	3492	3493	3494	3495	3496	3497	3498	3499

	0	1	2	3	4	5	6	7
6300	3072	3073	3074	3075	3076	3077	3078	3079
6301	3080	3081	3082	3083	3084	3085	3086	3087
6302	3088	3089	3090	3091	3092	3093	3094	3095
6303	3096	3097	3098	3099	3100	3101	3102	3103
6304	3104	3105	3106	3107	3108	3109	3110	3111
6305	3112	3113	3114	3115	3116	3117	3118	3119
6306	3120	3121	3122	3123	3124	3125	3126	3127
6307	3128	3129	3130	3131	3132	3133	3134	3135

	7	6	5	4	3	2	1	0
630	3271	3270	3269	3268	3267	3266	3265	3264
631	3279	3278	3277	3276	3275	3274	3273	3272
632	3287	3286	3285	3284	3283	3282	3281	3280
633	3295	3294	3293	3292	3291	3290	3289	3288
634	3303	3302	3301	3300	3299	3298	3297	3296
635	3311	3310	3309	3308	3307	3306	3305	3304
636	3319	3318	3317	3316	3315	3314	3313	3312
637	3327	3326	3325	3324	3323	3322	3321	3320

	7	6	5	4	3	2	1	0
620	3207	3206	3205	3204	3203	3202	3201	3200
621	3215	3214	3213	3212	3211	3210	3209	3208
622	3223	3222	3221	3220	3219	3218	3217	3216
623	3231	3230	3229	3228	3227	3226	3225	3224
624	3239	3238	3237	3236	3235	3234	3233	3232
625	3247	3246	3245	3244	3243	3242	3241	3240
626	3255	3254	3253	3252	3251	3250	3249	3248
627	3263	3262	3261	3260	3259	3258	3257	3256

	7	6	5	4	3	2	1	0
670	3527	3526	3525	3524	3523	3522	3521	3520
671	3535	3534	3533	3532	3531	3530	3529	3528
672	3543	3542	3541	3540	3539	3538	3537	3536
673	3551	3550	3549	3548	3547	3546	3545	3544
674	3559	3558	3557	3556	3555	3554	3553	3552
675	3567	3566	3565	3564	3563	3562	3561	3560
676	3575	3574	3573	3572	3571	3570	3569	3568
677	3583	3582	3581	3580	3579	3578	3577	3576

	7	6	5	4	3	2	1	0
660	3463	3462	3461	3460	3459	3458	3457	3456
661	3471	3470	3469	3468	3467	3466	3465	3464
662	3479	3478	3477	3476	3475	3474	3473	3472
663	3487	3486	3485	3484	3483	3482	3481	3480
664	3495	3494	3493	3492	3491	3490	3489	3488
665	3503	3502	3501	3500	3499	3498	3497	3496
666	3511	3510	3509	3508	3507	3506	3505	3504
667	3519	3518	3517	3516	3515	3514	3513	3512

7	3655	3663	3671	3679	3687	3695	3703	3711
6	3654	3662	3670	3678	3686	3694	3702	3710
5	3653	3661	3669	3677	3685	3693	3701	3709
4	3652	3660	3668	3676	3684	3692	3700	3708
3	3651	3659	3667	3675	3683	3691	3699	3707
2	3650	3658	3666	3674	3682	3690	3698	3706
1	3649	3657	3665	3673	3681	3689	3697	3705
0	3648	3656	3664	3672	3680	3688	3696	3704
	7240	7241	7242	7243	7244	7245	7246	7247

7	3591	3599	3607	3615	3623	3631	3639	3647
6	3590	3598	3606	3614	3622	3630	3638	3646
5	3589	3597	3605	3613	3621	3629	3637	3645
4	3588	3596	3604	3612	3620	3628	3636	3644
3	3587	3595	3603	3611	3619	3627	3635	3643
2	3586	3594	3602	3610	3618	3626	3634	3642
1	3585	3593	3601	3609	3617	3625	3633	3641
0	3584	3592	3600	3608	3616	3624	3632	3640
	7208	7209	7210	7211	7212	7213	7214	7215

	0	1	2	3	4	5	6	7
730	3776	3777	3778	3779	3780	3781	3782	3783
731	3784	3785	3786	3787	3788	3789	3790	3791
732	3792	3793	3794	3795	3796	3797	3798	3799
733	3800	3801	3802	3803	3804	3805	3806	3807
734	3808	3809	3810	3811	3812	3813	3814	3815
735	3816	3817	3818	3819	3820	3821	3822	3823
736	3824	3825	3826	3827	3828	3829	3830	3831
737	3832	3833	3834	3835	3836	3837	3838	3839

	0	1	2	3	4	5	6	7
720	3712	3713	3714	3715	3716	3717	3718	3719
721	3720	3721	3722	3723	3724	3725	3726	3727
722	3728	3729	3730	3731	3732	3733	3734	3735
723	3736	3737	3738	3739	3740	3741	3742	3743
724	3744	3745	3746	3747	3748	3749	3750	3751
725	3752	3753	3754	3755	3756	3757	3758	3759
726	3760	3761	3762	3763	3764	3765	3766	3767
727	3768	3769	3770	3771	3772	3773	3774	3775

	0	1	2	3	4	5	6	7
750	3904	3905	3906	3907	3908	3909	3910	3911
751	3912	3913	3914	3915	3916	3917	3918	3919
752	3920	3921	3922	3923	3924	3925	3926	3927
753	3928	3929	3930	3931	3932	3933	3934	3935
754	3936	3937	3938	3939	3940	3941	3942	3943
755	3944	3945	3946	3947	3948	3949	3950	3951
756	3952	3953	3954	3955	3956	3957	3958	3959
757	3960	3961	3962	3963	3964	3965	3966	3967

	0	1	2	3	4	5	6	7
740	3840	3841	3842	3843	3844	3845	3846	3847
741	3848	3849	3850	3851	3852	3853	3854	3855
742	3856	3857	3858	3859	3860	3861	3862	3863
743	3864	3865	3866	3867	3868	3869	3870	3871
744	3872	3873	3874	3875	3876	3877	3878	3879
745	3880	3881	3882	3883	3884	3885	3886	3887
746	3888	3889	3890	3891	3892	3893	3894	3895
747	3896	3897	3898	3899	3900	3901	3902	3903

	0	1	2	3	4	5	6	7
770	4032	4033	4034	4035	4036	4037	4038	4039
771	4040	4041	4042	4043	4044	4045	4046	4047
772	4048	4049	4050	4051	4052	4053	4054	4055
773	4056	4057	4058	4059	4060	4061	4062	4063
774	4064	4065	4066	4067	4068	4069	4070	4071
775	4072	4073	4074	4075	4076	4077	4078	4079
776	4080	4081	4082	4083	4084	4085	4086	4087
777	4088	4089	4090	4091	4092	4093	4094	4095

	0	1	2	3	4	5	6	7
760	3968	3969	3970	3971	3972	3973	3974	3975
761	3976	3977	3978	3979	3980	3981	3982	3983
762	3984	3985	3986	3987	3988	3989	3990	3991
763	3992	3993	3994	3995	3996	3997	3998	3999
764	4000	4001	4002	4003	4004	4005	4006	4007
765	4008	4009	4010	4011	4012	4013	4014	4015
766	4016	4017	4018	4019	4020	4021	4022	4023
767	4024	4025	4026	4027	4028	4029	4030	4031

NUMBER CONVERSION,
DECIMAL TO HEXADECIMAL AND VICE VERSA

DECIMAL TO HEXADECIMAL

Decimal numbers are listed sequentially in the main body. To convert to hexadecimal, locate the row (left hand two figures) and column (heading) corresponding to the required decimal value. The hexadecimal value is given by the two figures concatenated with the heading. For example, decimal 826 is equivalent to hexadecimal 33A.

HEXADECIMAL TO DECIMAL

The three digit hexadecimal number (with leading zeros if necessary) is located by its leading two figures (giving the row) the third (right hand) figure giving the column. The intersection of this row and column is the equivalent decimal value. For example, hexadecimal AF7 is equivalent to decimal 2807.

	0	1	2	3	4	5	6	7	8	9	A	B	C	D	E	F
00	0000	0001	0002	0003	0004	0005	0006	0007	0008	0009	0010	0011	0012	0013	0014	0015
01	0016	0017	0018	0019	0020	0021	0022	0023	0024	0025	0026	0027	0028	0029	0030	0031
02	0032	0033	0034	0035	0036	0037	0038	0039	0040	0041	0042	0043	0044	0045	0046	0047
03	0048	0049	0050	0051	0052	0053	0054	0055	0056	0057	0058	0059	0060	0061	0062	0063
04	0064	0065	0066	0067	0068	0069	0070	0071	0072	0073	0074	0075	0076	0077	0078	0079
05	0080	0081	0082	0083	0084	0085	0086	0087	0088	0089	0090	0091	0092	0093	0094	0095
06	0096	0097	0098	0099	0100	0101	0102	0103	0104	0105	0106	0107	0108	0109	0110	0111
07	0112	0113	0114	0115	0116	0117	0118	0119	0120	0121	0122	0123	0124	0125	0126	0127
08	0128	0129	0130	0131	0132	0133	0134	0135	0136	0137	0138	0139	0140	0141	0142	0143
09	0144	0145	0146	0147	0148	0149	0150	0151	0152	0153	0154	0155	0156	0157	0158	0159
0A	0160	0161	0162	0163	0164	0165	0166	0167	0168	0169	0170	0171	0172	0173	0174	0175
0B	0176	0177	0178	0179	0180	0181	0182	0183	0184	0185	0186	0187	0188	0189	0190	0191
0C	0192	0193	0194	0195	0196	0197	0198	0199	0200	0201	0202	0203	0204	0205	0206	0207
0D	0208	0209	0210	0211	0212	0213	0214	0215	0216	0217	0218	0219	0220	0221	0222	0223
0E	0224	0225	0226	0227	0228	0229	0230	0231	0232	0233	0234	0235	0236	0237	0238	0239
0F	0240	0241	0242	0243	0244	0245	0246	0247	0248	0249	0250	0251	0252	0253	0254	0255
10	0256	0257	0258	0259	0260	0261	0262	0263	0264	0265	0266	0267	0268	0269	0270	0271
11	0272	0273	0274	0275	0276	0277	0278	0279	0280	0281	0282	0283	0284	0285	0286	0287
12	0288	0289	0290	0291	0292	0293	0294	0295	0296	0297	0298	0299	0300	0301	0302	0303
13	0304	0305	0306	0307	0308	0309	0310	0311	0312	0313	0314	0315	0316	0317	0318	0319
14	0320	0321	0322	0323	0324	0325	0326	0327	0328	0329	0330	0331	0332	0333	0334	0335
15	0336	0337	0338	0339	0340	0341	0342	0343	0344	0345	0346	0347	0348	0349	0350	0351
16	0352	0353	0354	0355	0356	0357	0358	0359	0360	0361	0362	0363	0364	0365	0366	0367
17	0368	0369	0370	0371	0372	0373	0374	0375	0376	0377	0378	0379	0380	0381	0382	0383

	0	1	2	3	4	5	6	7	8	9	A	B	C	D	E	F
18	0384	0385	0386	0387	0388	0389	0390	0391	0392	0393	0394	0395	0396	0397	0398	0399
19	0400	0401	0402	0403	0404	0405	0406	0407	0408	0409	0410	0411	0412	0413	0414	0415
1A	0416	0417	0418	0419	0420	0421	0422	0423	0424	0425	0426	0427	0428	0429	0430	0431
1B	0432	0433	0434	0435	0436	0437	0438	0439	0440	0441	0442	0443	0444	0445	0446	0447
1C	0448	0449	0450	0451	0452	0453	0454	0455	0456	0457	0458	0459	0460	0461	0462	0463
1D	0464	0465	0466	0467	0468	0469	0470	0471	0472	0473	0474	0475	0476	0477	0478	0479
1E	0480	0481	0482	0483	0484	0485	0486	0487	0488	0489	0490	0491	0492	0493	0494	0495
1F	0496	0497	0498	0499	0500	0501	0502	0503	0504	0505	0506	0507	0508	0509	0510	0511
20	0512	0513	0514	0515	0516	0517	0518	0519	0520	0521	0522	0523	0524	0525	0526	0527
21	0528	0529	0530	0531	0532	0533	0534	0535	0536	0537	0538	0539	0540	0541	0542	0543
22	0544	0545	0546	0547	0548	0549	0550	0551	0552	0553	0554	0555	0556	0557	0558	0559
23	0560	0561	0562	0563	0564	0565	0566	0567	0568	0569	0570	0571	0572	0573	0574	0575
24	0576	0577	0578	0579	0580	0581	0582	0583	0584	0585	0586	0587	0588	0589	0590	0591
25	0592	0593	0594	0595	0596	0597	0598	0599	0600	0601	0602	0603	0604	0605	0606	0607
26	0608	0609	0610	0611	0612	0613	0614	0615	0616	0617	0618	0619	0620	0621	0622	0623
27	0624	0625	0626	0627	0628	0629	0630	0631	0632	0633	0634	0635	0636	0637	0638	0639
28	0640	0641	0642	0643	0644	0645	0646	0647	0648	0649	0650	0651	0652	0653	0654	0655
29	0656	0657	0658	0659	0660	0661	0662	0663	0664	0665	0666	0667	0668	0669	0670	0671
2A	0672	0673	0674	0675	0676	0677	0678	0679	0680	0681	0682	0683	0684	0685	0686	0687
2B	0688	0689	0690	0691	0692	0693	0694	0695	0696	0697	0698	0699	0700	0701	0702	0703
2C	0704	0705	0706	0707	0708	0709	0710	0711	0712	0713	0714	0715	0716	0717	0718	0719
2D	0720	0721	0722	0723	0724	0725	0726	0727	0728	0729	0730	0731	0732	0733	0734	0735
2E	0736	0737	0738	0739	0740	0741	0742	0743	0744	0745	0746	0747	0748	0749	0750	0751
2F	0752	0753	0754	0755	0756	0757	0758	0759	0760	0761	0762	0763	0764	0765	0766	0767

	0	1	2	3	4	5	6	7	8	9	A	B	C	D	E	F
30	0768	0769	0770	0771	0772	0773	0774	0775	0776	0777	0778	0779	0780	0781	0782	0783
31	0784	0785	0786	0787	0788	0789	0790	0791	0792	0793	0794	0795	0796	0797	0798	0799
32	0800	0801	0802	0803	0804	0805	0806	0807	0808	0809	0810	0811	0812	0813	0814	0815
33	0816	0817	0818	0819	0820	0821	0822	0823	0824	0825	0826	0827	0828	0829	0830	0831
34	0832	0833	0834	0835	0836	0837	0838	0839	0840	0841	0842	0843	0844	0845	0846	0847
35	0848	0849	0850	0851	0852	0853	0854	0855	0856	0857	0858	0859	0860	0861	0862	0863
36	0864	0865	0866	0867	0868	0869	0870	0871	0872	0873	0874	0875	0876	0877	0878	0879
37	0880	0881	0882	0883	0884	0885	0886	0887	0888	0889	0890	0891	0892	0893	0894	0895
38	0896	0897	0898	0899	0900	0901	0902	0903	0904	0905	0906	0907	0908	0909	0910	0911
39	0912	0913	0914	0915	0916	0917	0918	0919	0920	0921	0922	0923	0924	0925	0926	0927
3A	0928	0929	0930	0931	0932	0933	0934	0935	0936	0937	0938	0939	0940	0941	0942	0943
3B	0944	0945	0946	0947	0948	0949	0950	0951	0952	0953	0954	0955	0956	0957	0958	0959
3C	0960	0961	0962	0963	0964	0965	0966	0967	0968	0969	0970	0971	0972	0973	0974	0975
3D	0976	0977	0978	0979	0980	0981	0982	0983	0984	0985	0986	0987	0988	0989	0990	0991
3E	0992	0993	0994	0995	0996	0997	0998	0999	1000	1001	1002	1003	1004	1005	1006	1007
3F	1008	1009	1010	1011	1012	1013	1014	1015	1016	1017	1018	1019	1020	1021	1022	1023
40	1024	1025	1026	1027	1028	1029	1030	1031	1032	1033	1034	1035	1036	1037	1038	1039
41	1040	1041	1042	1043	1044	1045	1046	1047	1048	1049	1050	1051	1052	1053	1054	1055
42	1056	1057	1058	1059	1060	1061	1062	1063	1064	1065	1066	1067	1068	1069	1070	1071
43	1072	1073	1074	1075	1076	1077	1078	1079	1080	1081	1082	1083	1084	1085	1086	1087
44	1088	1089	1090	1091	1092	1093	1094	1095	1096	1097	1098	1099	1100	1101	1102	1103
45	1104	1105	1106	1107	1108	1109	1110	1111	1112	1113	1114	1115	1116	1117	1118	1119
46	1120	1121	1122	1123	1124	1125	1126	1127	1128	1129	1130	1131	1132	1133	1134	1135
47	1136	1137	1138	1139	1140	1141	1142	1143	1144	1145	1146	1147	1148	1149	1150	1151

	0	1	2	3	4	5	6	7	8	9	A	B	C	D	E	F
48	1152	1153	1154	1155	1156	1157	1158	1159	1160	1161	1162	1163	1164	1165	1166	1167
49	1168	1169	1170	1171	1172	1173	1174	1175	1176	1177	1178	1179	1180	1181	1182	1183
4A	1184	1185	1186	1187	1188	1189	1190	1191	1192	1193	1194	1195	1196	1197	1198	1199
4B	1200	1201	1202	1203	1204	1205	1206	1207	1208	1209	1210	1211	1212	1213	1214	1215
4C	1216	1217	1218	1219	1220	1221	1222	1223	1224	1225	1226	1227	1228	1229	1230	1231
4D	1232	1233	1234	1235	1236	1237	1238	1239	1240	1241	1242	1243	1244	1245	1246	1247
4E	1248	1249	1250	1251	1252	1253	1254	1255	1256	1257	1258	1259	1260	1261	1262	1263
4F	1264	1265	1266	1267	1268	1269	1270	1271	1272	1273	1274	1275	1276	1277	1278	1279
50	1280	1281	1282	1283	1284	1285	1286	1287	1288	1289	1290	1291	1292	1293	1294	1295
51	1296	1297	1298	1299	1300	1301	1302	1303	1304	1305	1306	1307	1308	1309	1310	1311
52	1312	1313	1314	1315	1316	1317	1318	1319	1320	1321	1322	1323	1324	1325	1326	1327
53	1328	1329	1330	1331	1332	1333	1334	1335	1336	1337	1338	1339	1340	1341	1342	1343
54	1344	1345	1346	1347	1348	1349	1350	1351	1352	1353	1354	1355	1356	1357	1358	1359
55	1360	1361	1362	1363	1364	1365	1366	1367	1368	1369	1370	1371	1372	1373	1374	1375
56	1376	1377	1378	1379	1380	1381	1382	1383	1384	1385	1386	1387	1388	1389	1390	1391
57	1392	1393	1394	1395	1396	1397	1398	1399	1400	1401	1402	1403	1404	1405	1406	1407
58	1408	1409	1410	1411	1412	1413	1414	1415	1416	1417	1418	1419	1420	1421	1422	1423
59	1424	1425	1426	1427	1428	1429	1430	1431	1432	1433	1434	1435	1436	1437	1438	1439
5A	1440	1441	1442	1443	1444	1445	1446	1447	1448	1449	1450	1451	1452	1453	1454	1455
5B	1456	1457	1458	1459	1460	1461	1462	1463	1464	1465	1466	1467	1468	1469	1470	1471
5C	1472	1473	1474	1475	1476	1477	1478	1479	1480	1481	1482	1483	1484	1485	1486	1487
5D	1488	1489	1490	1491	1492	1493	1494	1495	1496	1497	1498	1499	1500	1501	1502	1503
5E	1504	1505	1506	1507	1508	1509	1510	1511	1512	1513	1514	1515	1516	1517	1518	1519
5F	1520	1521	1522	1523	1524	1525	1526	1527	1528	1529	1530	1531	1532	1533	1534	1535

	0	1	2	3	4	5	6	7	8	9	A	B	C	D	E	F
60	1536	1537	1538	1539	1540	1541	1542	1543	1544	1545	1546	1547	1548	1549	1550	1551
61	1552	1553	1554	1555	1556	1557	1558	1559	1560	1561	1562	1563	1564	1565	1566	1567
62	1568	1569	1570	1571	1572	1573	1574	1575	1576	1577	1578	1579	1580	1581	1582	1583
63	1584	1585	1586	1587	1588	1589	1590	1591	1592	1593	1594	1595	1596	1597	1598	1599
64	1600	1601	1602	1603	1604	1605	1606	1607	1608	1609	1610	1611	1612	1613	1614	1615
65	1616	1617	1618	1619	1620	1621	1622	1623	1624	1625	1626	1627	1628	1629	1630	1631
66	1632	1633	1634	1635	1636	1637	1638	1639	1640	1641	1642	1643	1644	1645	1646	1647
67	1648	1649	1650	1651	1652	1653	1654	1655	1656	1657	1658	1659	1660	1661	1662	1663
68	1664	1665	1666	1667	1668	1669	1670	1671	1672	1673	1674	1675	1676	1677	1678	1679
69	1680	1681	1682	1683	1684	1685	1686	1687	1688	1689	1690	1691	1692	1693	1694	1695
6A	1696	1697	1698	1699	1700	1701	1702	1703	1704	1705	1706	1707	1708	1709	1710	1711
6B	1712	1713	1714	1715	1716	1717	1718	1719	1720	1721	1722	1723	1724	1725	1726	1727
6C	1728	1729	1730	1731	1732	1733	1734	1735	1736	1737	1738	1739	1740	1741	1742	1743
6D	1744	1745	1746	1747	1748	1749	1750	1751	1752	1753	1754	1755	1756	1757	1758	1759
6E	1760	1761	1762	1763	1764	1765	1766	1767	1768	1769	1770	1771	1772	1773	1774	1775
6F	1776	1777	1778	1779	1780	1781	1782	1783	1784	1785	1786	1787	1788	1789	1790	1791
70	1792	1793	1794	1795	1796	1797	1798	1799	1800	1801	1802	1803	1804	1805	1806	1807
71	1808	1809	1810	1811	1812	1813	1814	1815	1816	1817	1818	1819	1820	1821	1822	1823
72	1824	1825	1826	1827	1828	1829	1830	1831	1832	1833	1834	1835	1836	1837	1838	1839
73	1840	1841	1842	1843	1844	1845	1846	1847	1848	1849	1850	1851	1852	1853	1854	1855
74	1856	1857	1858	1859	1860	1861	1862	1863	1864	1865	1866	1867	1868	1869	1870	1871
75	1872	1873	1874	1875	1876	1877	1878	1879	1880	1881	1882	1883	1884	1885	1886	1887
76	1888	1889	1890	1891	1892	1893	1894	1895	1896	1897	1898	1899	1900	1901	1902	1903
77	1904	1905	1906	1907	1908	1909	1910	1911	1912	1913	1914	1915	1916	1917	1918	1919

	0	1	2	3	4	5	6	7	8	9	A	B	C	D	E	F
78	1920	1921	1922	1923	1924	1925	1926	1927	1928	1929	1930	1931	1932	1933	1934	1935
79	1936	1937	1938	1939	1940	1941	1942	1943	1944	1945	1946	1947	1948	1949	1950	1951
7A	1952	1953	1954	1955	1956	1957	1958	1959	1960	1961	1962	1963	1964	1965	1966	1967
7B	1968	1969	1970	1971	1972	1973	1974	1975	1976	1977	1978	1979	1980	1981	1982	1983
7C	1984	1985	1986	1987	1988	1989	1990	1991	1992	1993	1994	1995	1996	1997	1998	1999
7D	2000	2001	2002	2003	2004	2005	2006	2007	2008	2009	2010	2011	2012	2013	2014	2015
7E	2016	2017	2018	2019	2020	2021	2022	2023	2024	2025	2026	2027	2028	2029	2030	2031
7F	2032	2033	2034	2035	2036	2037	2038	2039	2040	2041	2042	2043	2044	2045	2046	2047
80	2048	2049	2050	2051	2052	2053	2054	2055	2056	2057	2058	2059	2060	2061	2062	2063
81	2064	2065	2066	2067	2068	2069	2070	2071	2072	2073	2074	2075	2076	2077	2078	2079
82	2080	2081	2082	2083	2084	2085	2086	2087	2088	2089	2090	2091	2092	2093	2094	2095
83	2096	2097	2098	2099	2100	2101	2102	2103	2104	2105	2106	2107	2108	2109	2110	2111
84	2112	2113	2114	2115	2116	2117	2118	2119	2120	2121	2122	2123	2124	2125	2126	2127
85	2128	2129	2130	2131	2132	2133	2134	2135	2136	2137	2138	2139	2140	2141	2142	2143
86	2144	2145	2146	2147	2148	2149	2150	2151	2152	2153	2154	2155	2156	2157	2158	2159
87	2160	2161	2162	2163	2164	2165	2166	2167	2168	2169	2170	2171	2172	2173	2174	2175
88	2176	2177	2178	2179	2180	2181	2182	2183	2184	2185	2186	2187	2188	2189	2190	2191
89	2192	2193	2194	2195	2196	2197	2198	2199	2200	2201	2202	2203	2204	2205	2206	2207
8A	2208	2209	2210	2211	2212	2213	2214	2215	2216	2217	2218	2219	2220	2221	2222	2223
8B	2224	2225	2226	2227	2228	2229	2230	2231	2232	2233	2234	2235	2236	2237	2238	2239
8C	2240	2241	2242	2243	2244	2245	2246	2247	2248	2249	2250	2251	2252	2253	2254	2255
8D	2256	2257	2258	2259	2260	2261	2262	2263	2264	2265	2266	2267	2268	2269	2270	2271
8E	2272	2273	2274	2275	2276	2277	2278	2279	2280	2281	2282	2283	2284	2285	2286	2287
8F	2288	2289	2290	2291	2292	2293	2294	2295	2296	2297	2298	2299	2300	2301	2302	2303

	0	1	2	3	4	5	6	7	8	9	A	B	C	D	E	F
90	2304	2305	2306	2307	2308	2309	2310	2311	2312	2313	2314	2315	2316	2317	2318	2319
91	2320	2321	2322	2323	2324	2325	2326	2327	2328	2329	2330	2331	2332	2333	2334	2335
92	2336	2337	2338	2339	2340	2341	2342	2343	2344	2345	2346	2347	2348	2349	2350	2351
93	2352	2353	2354	2355	2356	2357	2358	2359	2360	2361	2362	2363	2364	2365	2366	2367
94	2368	2369	2370	2371	2372	2373	2374	2375	2376	2377	2378	2379	2380	2381	2382	2383
95	2384	2385	2386	2387	2388	2389	2390	2391	2392	2393	2394	2395	2396	2397	2398	2399
96	2400	2401	2402	2403	2404	2405	2406	2407	2408	2409	2410	2411	2412	2413	2414	2415
97	2416	2417	2418	2419	2420	2421	2422	2423	2424	2425	2426	2427	2428	2429	2430	2431
98	2432	2433	2434	2435	2436	2437	2438	2439	2440	2441	2442	2443	2444	2445	2446	2447
99	2448	2449	2450	2451	2452	2453	2454	2455	2456	2457	2458	2459	2460	2461	2462	2463
9A	2464	2465	2466	2467	2468	2469	2470	2471	2472	2473	2474	2475	2476	2477	2478	2479
9B	2480	2481	2482	2483	2484	2485	2486	2487	2488	2489	2490	2491	2492	2493	2494	2495
9C	2496	2497	2498	2499	2500	2501	2502	2503	2504	2505	2506	2507	2508	2509	2510	2511
9D	2512	2513	2514	2515	2516	2517	2518	2519	2520	2521	2522	2523	2524	2525	2526	2527
9E	2528	2529	2530	2531	2532	2533	2534	2535	2536	2537	2538	2539	2540	2541	2542	2543
9F	2544	2545	2546	2547	2548	2549	2550	2551	2552	2553	2554	2555	2556	2557	2558	2559
A0	2560	2561	2562	2563	2564	2565	2566	2567	2568	2569	2570	2571	2572	2573	2574	2575
A1	2576	2577	2578	2579	2580	2581	2582	2583	2584	2585	2586	2587	2588	2589	2590	2591
A2	2592	2593	2594	2595	2596	2597	2598	2599	2600	2601	2602	2603	2604	2605	2606	2607
A3	2608	2609	2610	2611	2612	2613	2614	2615	2616	2617	2618	2619	2620	2621	2622	2623
A4	2624	2625	2626	2627	2628	2629	2630	2631	2632	2633	2634	2635	2636	2637	2638	2639
A5	2640	2641	2642	2643	2644	2645	2646	2647	2648	2649	2650	2651	2652	2653	2654	2655
A6	2656	2657	2658	2659	2660	2661	2662	2663	2664	2665	2666	2667	2668	2669	2670	2671
A7	2672	2673	2674	2675	2676	2677	2678	2679	2680	2681	2682	2683	2684	2685	2686	2687

	0	1	2	3	4	5	6	7	8	9	A	B	C	D	E	F
A8	2688	2689	2690	2691	2692	2693	2694	2695	2696	2697	2698	2699	2700	2701	2702	2703
A9	2704	2705	2706	2707	2708	2709	2710	2711	2712	2713	2714	2715	2716	2717	2718	2719
AA	2720	2721	2722	2723	2724	2725	2726	2727	2728	2729	2730	2731	2732	2733	2734	2735
AB	2736	2737	2738	2739	2740	2741	2742	2743	2744	2745	2746	2747	2748	2749	2750	2751
AC	2752	2753	2754	2755	2756	2757	2758	2759	2760	2761	2762	2763	2764	2765	2766	2767
AD	2768	2769	2770	2771	2772	2773	2774	2775	2776	2777	2778	2779	2780	2781	2782	2783
AE	2784	2785	2786	2787	2788	2789	2790	2791	2792	2793	2794	2795	2796	2797	2798	2799
AF	2800	2801	2802	2803	2804	2805	2806	2807	2808	2809	2810	2811	2812	2813	2814	2815
B0	2816	2817	2818	2819	2820	2821	2822	2823	2824	2825	2826	2827	2828	2829	2830	2831
B1	2832	2833	2834	2835	2836	2837	2838	2839	2840	2841	2842	2843	2844	2845	2846	2847
B2	2848	2849	2850	2851	2852	2853	2854	2855	2856	2857	2858	2859	2860	2861	2862	2863
B3	2864	2865	2866	2867	2868	2869	2870	2871	2872	2873	2874	2875	2876	2877	2878	2879
B4	2880	2881	2882	2883	2884	2885	2886	2887	2888	2889	2890	2891	2892	2893	2894	2895
B5	2896	2897	2898	2899	2900	2901	2902	2903	2904	2905	2906	2907	2908	2909	2910	2911
B6	2912	2913	2914	2915	2916	2917	2918	2919	2920	2921	2922	2923	2924	2925	2926	2927
B7	2928	2929	2930	2931	2932	2933	2934	2935	2936	2937	2938	2939	2940	2941	2942	2943
B8	2944	2945	2946	2947	2948	2949	2950	2951	2952	2953	2954	2955	2956	2957	2958	2959
B9	2960	2961	2962	2963	2964	2965	2966	2967	2968	2969	2970	2971	2972	2973	2974	2975
BA	2976	2977	2978	2979	2980	2981	2982	2983	2984	2985	2986	2987	2988	2989	2990	2991
BB	2992	2993	2994	2995	2996	2997	2998	2999	3000	3001	3002	3003	3004	3005	3006	3007
BC	3008	3009	3010	3011	3012	3013	3014	3015	3016	3017	3018	3019	3020	3021	3022	3023
BD	3024	3025	3026	3027	3028	3029	3030	3031	3032	3033	3034	3035	3036	3037	3038	3039
BE	3040	3041	3042	3043	3044	3045	3046	3047	3048	3049	3050	3051	3052	3053	3054	3055
BF	3056	3057	3058	3059	3060	3061	3062	3063	3064	3065	3066	3067	3068	3069	3070	3071

	0	1	2	3	4	5	6	7	8	9	A	B	C	D	E	F
C0	3072	3073	3074	3075	3076	3077	3078	3079	3080	3081	3082	3083	3084	3085	3086	3087
C1	3088	3089	3090	3091	3092	3093	3094	3095	3096	3097	3098	3099	3100	3101	3102	3103
C2	3104	3105	3106	3107	3108	3109	3110	3111	3112	3113	3114	3115	3116	3117	3118	3119
C3	3120	3121	3122	3123	3124	3125	3126	3127	3128	3129	3130	3131	3132	3133	3134	3135
C4	3136	3137	3138	3139	3140	3141	3142	3143	3144	3145	3146	3147	3148	3149	3150	3151
C5	3152	3153	3154	3155	3156	3157	3158	3159	3160	3161	3162	3163	3164	3165	3166	3167
C6	3168	3169	3170	3171	3172	3173	3174	3175	3176	3177	3178	3179	3180	3181	3182	3183
C7	3184	3185	3186	3187	3188	3189	3190	3191	3192	3193	3194	3195	3196	3197	3198	3199
C8	3200	3201	3202	3203	3204	3205	3206	3207	3208	3209	3210	3211	3212	3213	3214	3215
C9	3216	3217	3218	3219	3220	3221	3222	3223	3224	3225	3226	3227	3228	3229	3230	3231
CA	3232	3233	3234	3235	3236	3237	3238	3239	3240	3241	3242	3243	3244	3245	3246	3247
CB	3248	3249	3250	3251	3252	3253	3254	3255	3256	3257	3258	3259	3260	3261	3262	3263
CC	3264	3265	3266	3267	3268	3269	3270	3271	3272	3273	3274	3275	3276	3277	3278	3279
CD	3280	3281	3282	3283	3284	3285	3286	3287	3288	3289	3290	3291	3292	3293	3294	3295
CE	3296	3297	3298	3299	3300	3301	3302	3303	3304	3305	3306	3307	3308	3309	3310	3311
CF	3312	3313	3314	3315	3316	3317	3318	3319	3320	3321	3322	3323	3324	3325	3326	3327
D0	3328	3329	3330	3331	3332	3333	3334	3335	3336	3337	3338	3339	3340	3341	3342	3343
D1	3344	3345	3346	3347	3348	3349	3350	3351	3352	3353	3354	3355	3356	3357	3358	3359
D2	3360	3361	3362	3363	3364	3365	3366	3367	3368	3369	3370	3371	3372	3373	3374	3375
D3	3376	3377	3378	3379	3380	3381	3382	3383	3384	3385	3386	3387	3388	3389	3390	3391
D4	3392	3393	3394	3395	3396	3397	3398	3399	3400	3401	3402	3403	3404	3405	3406	3407
D5	3408	3409	3410	3411	3412	3413	3414	3415	3416	3417	3418	3419	3420	3421	3422	3423
D6	3424	3425	3426	3427	3428	3429	3430	3431	3432	3433	3434	3435	3436	3437	3438	3439
D7	3440	3441	3442	3443	3444	3445	3446	3447	3448	3449	3450	3451	3452	3453	3454	3455

	0	1	2	3	4	5	6	7	8	9	A	B	C	D	E	F
D8	3456	3457	3458	3459	3460	3461	3462	3463	3464	3465	3466	3467	3468	3469	3470	3471
D9	3472	3473	3474	3475	3476	3477	3478	3479	3480	3481	3482	3483	3484	3485	3486	3487
DA	3488	3489	3490	3491	3492	3493	3494	3495	3496	3497	3498	3499	3500	3501	3502	3503
DB	3504	3505	3506	3507	3508	3509	3510	3511	3512	3513	3514	3515	3516	3517	3518	3519
DC	3520	3521	3522	3523	3524	3525	3526	3527	3528	3529	3530	3531	3532	3533	3534	3535
DD	3536	3537	3538	3539	3540	3541	3542	3543	3544	3545	3546	3547	3548	3549	3550	3551
DE	3552	3553	3554	3555	3556	3557	3558	3559	3560	3561	3562	3563	3564	3565	3566	3567
DF	3568	3569	3570	3571	3572	3573	3574	3575	3576	3577	3578	3579	3580	3581	3582	3583
E0	3584	3585	3586	3587	3588	3589	3590	3591	3592	3593	3594	3595	3596	3597	3598	3599
E1	3600	3601	3602	3603	3604	3605	3606	3607	3608	3609	3610	3611	3612	3613	3614	3615
E2	3616	3617	3618	3619	3620	3621	3622	3623	3624	3625	3626	3627	3628	3629	3630	3631
E3	3632	3633	3634	3635	3636	3637	3638	3639	3640	3641	3642	3643	3644	3645	3646	3647
E4	3648	3649	3650	3651	3652	3653	3654	3655	3656	3657	3658	3659	3660	3661	3662	3663
E5	3664	3665	3666	3667	3668	3669	3670	3671	3672	3673	3674	3675	3676	3677	3678	3679
E6	3680	3681	3682	3683	3684	3685	3686	3687	3688	3689	3690	3691	3692	3693	3694	3695
E7	3696	3697	3698	3699	3700	3701	3702	3703	3704	3705	3706	3707	3708	3709	3710	3711
E8	3712	3713	3714	3715	3716	3717	3718	3719	3720	3721	3722	3723	3724	3725	3726	3727
E9	3728	3729	3730	3731	3732	3733	3734	3735	3736	3737	3738	3739	3740	3741	3742	3743
EA	3744	3745	3746	3747	3748	3749	3750	3751	3752	3753	3754	3755	3756	3757	3758	3759
EB	3760	3761	3762	3763	3764	3765	3766	3767	3768	3769	3770	3771	3772	3773	3774	3775
EC	3776	3777	3778	3779	3780	3781	3782	3783	3784	3785	3786	3787	3788	3789	3790	3791
ED	3792	3793	3794	3795	3796	3797	3798	3799	3800	3801	3802	3803	3804	3805	3806	3807
EE	3808	3809	3810	3811	3812	3813	3814	3815	3816	3817	3818	3819	3820	3821	3822	3823
EF	3824	3825	3826	3827	3828	3829	3830	3831	3832	3833	3834	3835	3836	3837	3838	3839

	0	1	2	3	4	5	6	7	8	9	A	B	C	D	E	F
F0	3840	3841	3842	3843	3844	3845	3846	3847	3848	3849	3850	3851	3852	3853	3854	3855
F1	3856	3857	3858	3859	3860	3861	3862	3863	3864	3865	3866	3867	3868	3869	3870	3871
F2	3872	3873	3874	3875	3876	3877	3878	3879	3880	3881	3882	3883	3884	3885	3886	3887
F3	3888	3889	3890	3891	3892	3893	3894	3895	3896	3897	3898	3899	3900	3901	3902	3903
F4	3904	3805	3906	3907	3908	3909	3910	3911	3912	3913	3914	3915	3916	3917	3918	3919
F5	3920	3921	3922	3923	3924	3925	3926	3927	3928	3929	3930	3931	3932	3933	3934	3935
F6	3936	3937	3938	3939	3940	3941	3942	3943	3944	3945	3946	3947	3948	3949	3950	3951
F7	3952	3953	3954	3955	3956	3957	3958	3959	3960	3961	3962	3963	3964	3965	3966	3967
F8	3968	3969	3970	3971	3972	3973	3974	3975	3976	3977	3978	3979	3980	3981	3982	3983
F9	3984	3985	3986	3987	3988	3989	3990	3991	3992	3993	3994	3995	3996	3997	3998	3999
FA	4000	4001	4002	4003	4004	4005	4006	4007	4008	4009	4010	4011	4012	4013	4014	4015
FB	4016	4017	4018	4019	4020	4021	4022	4023	4024	4025	4026	4027	4028	4029	4030	4031
FC	4032	4033	4034	4035	4036	4037	4038	4039	4040	4041	4042	4043	4044	4045	4046	4047
FD	4048	4049	4050	4051	4052	4053	4054	4055	4056	4057	4058	4059	4060	4061	4062	4063
FE	4064	4065	4066	4067	4068	4069	4070	4071	4072	4073	4074	4075	4076	4077	4078	4079
FF	4080	4081	4082	4083	4084	4085	4086	4087	4088	4089	4090	4091	4092	4093	4094	4095

5 Symbols

FLOWCHART SYMBOLS

1. SYSTEM

punched card

paper tape

magnetic tape

document

disc (or other on-line) storage

manual process

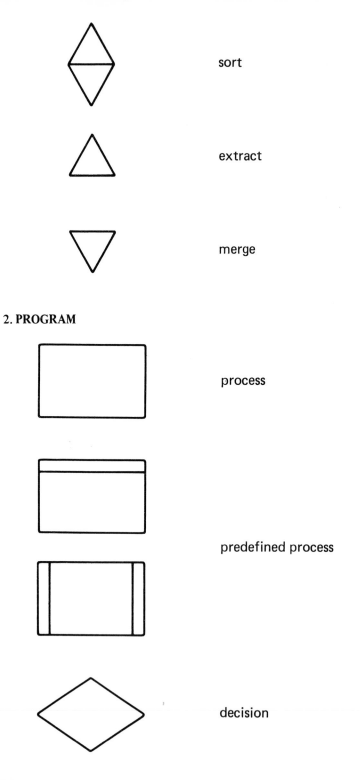

sort

extract

merge

2. PROGRAM

process

predefined process

decision

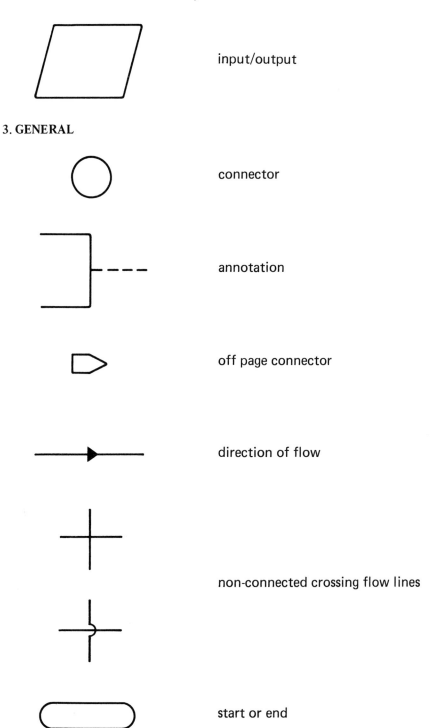

input/output

3. GENERAL

connector

annotation

off page connector

direction of flow

non-connected crossing flow lines

start or end

LOGIC

SYMBOLS FOR ELECTRONIC GATES

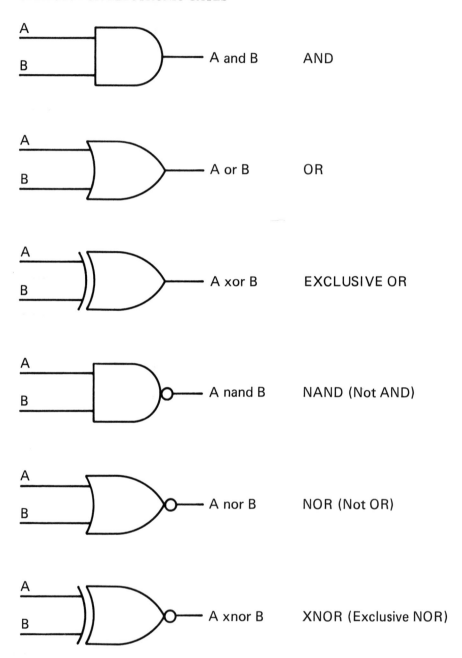

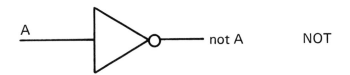

not A   NOT

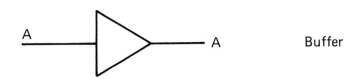

A   Buffer

TRUTH TABLES FOR ELECTRONIC GATES

AND	A	B	A and B
	0	0	0
	0	1	0
	1	0	0
	1	1	1

OR	A	B	A or B
	0	0	0
	0	1	1
	1	0	1
	1	1	1

XOR	A	B	A xor B
	0	0	0
	0	1	1
	1	0	1
	1	1	0

NAND	A	B	A nand B
	0	0	1
	0	1	1
	1	0	1
	1	1	0

NOR	A	B	A nor B
	0	0	1
	0	1	0
	1	0	0
	1	1	0

XNOR	A	B	A xnor B
	0	0	1
	0	1	0
	1	0	0
	1	1	1

NOT	A	not A
	0	1
	1	0

SYMBOLS FOR ELECTRICAL AND ELECTRONIC COMPONENTS

 Resistor

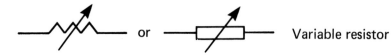 Variable resistor

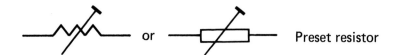 Preset resistor

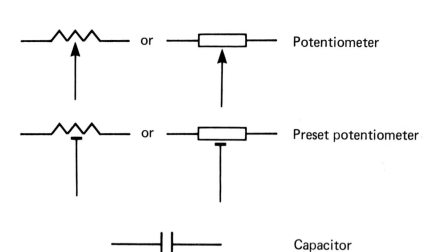

Potentiometer

Preset potentiometer

Capacitor

 Variable capacitor

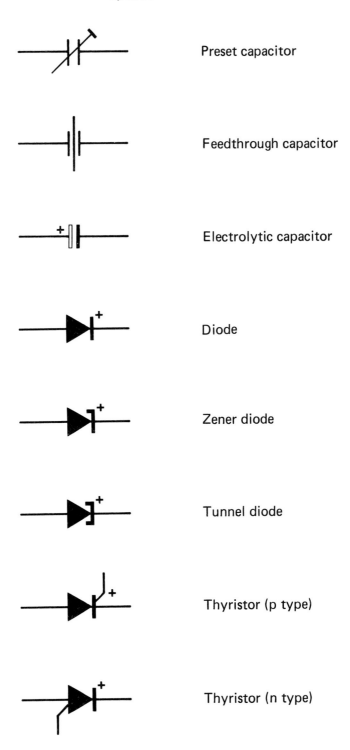

Preset capacitor

Feedthrough capacitor

Electrolytic capacitor

Diode

Zener diode

Tunnel diode

Thyristor (p type)

Thyristor (n type)

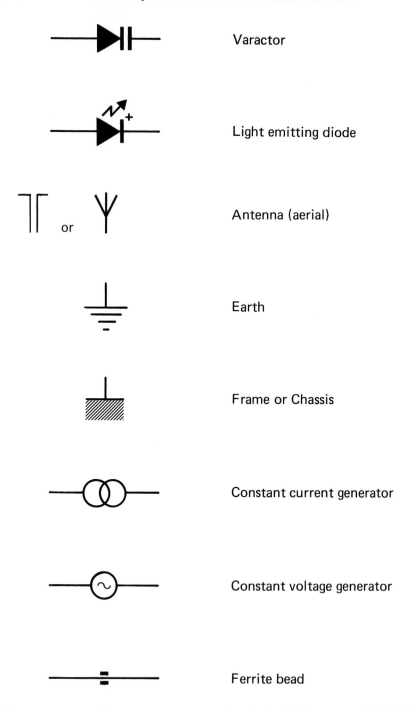

Varactor

Light emitting diode

Antenna (aerial)

Earth

Frame or Chassis

Constant current generator

Constant voltage generator

Ferrite bead

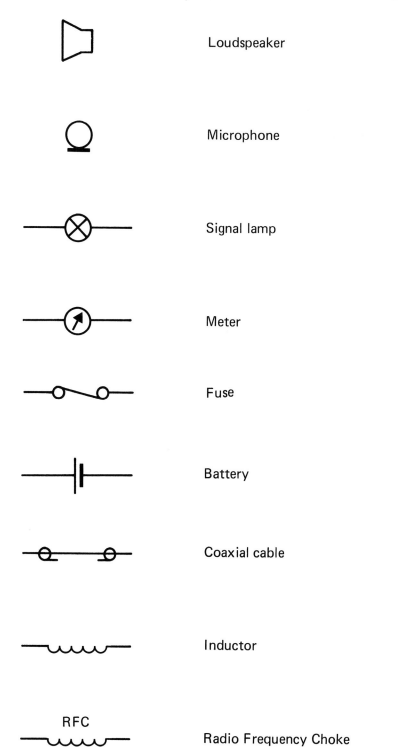

Loudspeaker

Microphone

Signal lamp

Meter

Fuse

Battery

Coaxial cable

Inductor

Radio Frequency Choke

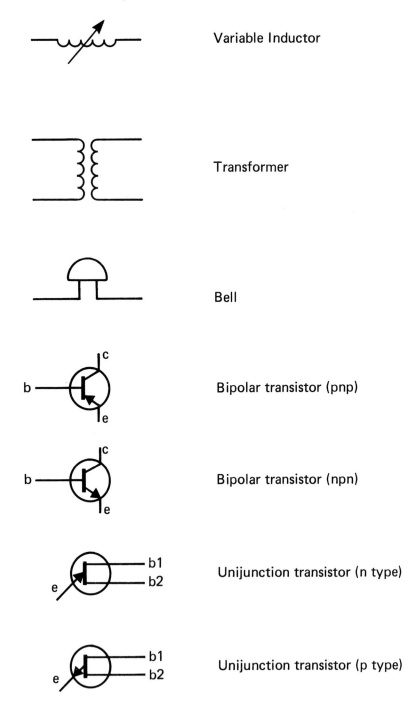

Variable Inductor

Transformer

Bell

Bipolar transistor (pnp)

Bipolar transistor (npn)

Unijunction transistor (n type)

Unijunction transistor (p type)

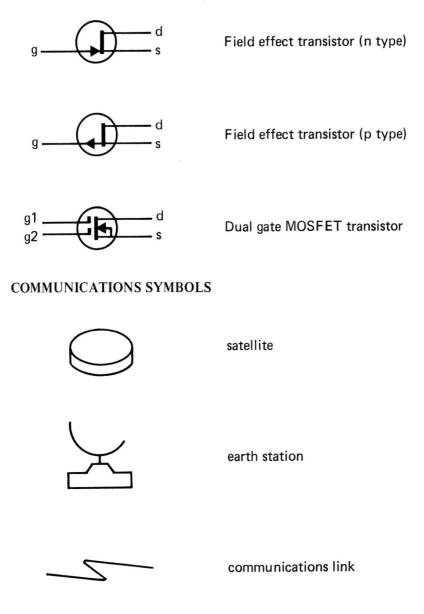

Field effect transistor (n type)

Field effect transistor (p type)

Dual gate MOSFET transistor

COMMUNICATIONS SYMBOLS

satellite

earth station

communications link

transmission line

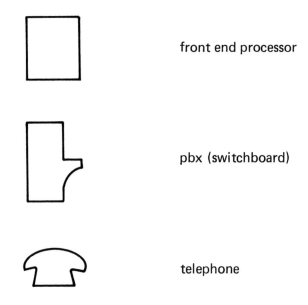

front end processor

pbx (switchboard)

telephone

DATA TRANSMISSION SYMBOLS

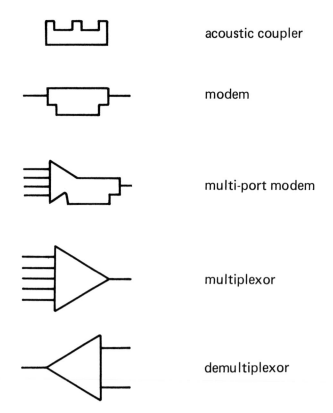

acoustic coupler

modem

multi-port modem

multiplexor

demultiplexor

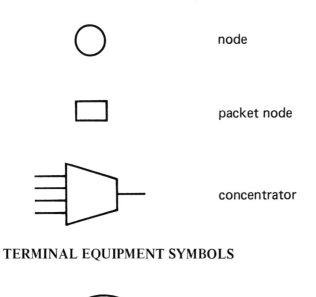

node

packet node

concentrator

TERMINAL EQUIPMENT SYMBOLS

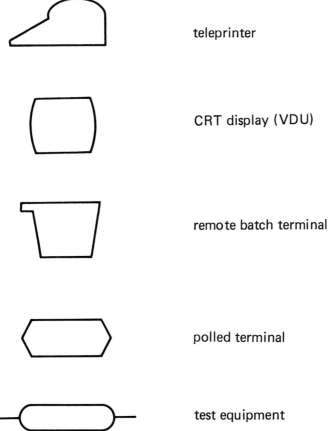

teleprinter

CRT display (VDU)

remote batch terminal

polled terminal

test equipment

6 International Standards

CCITT RECOMMENDATIONS

CATEGORIES

Series	Coverage
A	Organisation of CCITT
B	Means of Expression
C	Telecommunications Statistics
D	Tariff Principles, Leased Circuits
E	Telephone Operation, Quality of Service and Tariffs
F	Telegraph Operation and Tariffs
G	Line Transmission
H	Transmission of Signals other than Telephone
J	Sound Programme and Television Transmission
K	Protection against Interference
L	Protection of Cable Sheaths and Poles
M	Maintenance for Telephony, Telegraphy and Data Transmission
N	Maintenance for Sound Programme and Television Transmission
O	Specifications for Measuring Equipment
P	Quality of Telephone Transmission
Q	Telephone Signalling and Switching
R	Telegraph Transmission
S	Alphabetic Telegraph and Data Terminal Equipment
T	Facsimile
U	Telegraph Switching
V	Data Transmission over the Telephone Network
X	Data Transmission over Public Data Networks

INTERNATIONAL STANDARDS RELEVANT TO COMPUTING

1. DEFINITIONS

ISO	2382 pt 1	Fundamental terms
BS	3527/1	
ISO	2382 pt 2	Mathematics and Logic
BS	3527/2	
ISO	2382 pt 3	Equipment Technology
BS	3527/3	
ISO	2382 pt 4	Organisation of Data
BS	3527/4	

| ISO | 2382 pt 5 | Representation of Data |
| BS | 3527/5 | |

| ISO | 2382 pt 6 | Preparation and Handling of Data |
| BS | 3527/6 | |

| ISO | 2382 pt 7 | Digital Computer Programming |
| BS | 3527/7 | |

| ISO | 2382 pt 9 | Data Communication |
| BS | 3527/9 | |

| ISO | 2382 pt 10 | Operating Techniques and Facilities |
| BS | 3527/10 | |

| ISO | 2382 pt 11 | Control, Input/Output and Arithmetic Equipment |
| BS | 3527/11 | |

| ISO | 2382 pt 12 | Data Media, Storage and Data Carrier Equipment |
| BS | 3527/12 | |

| ISO | 2382 pt 14 | Reliability, Maintenance and Availability |
| BS | 3527/14 | |

| ISO | 2382 pt 16 | Information Theory |
| BS | 3527/16 | |

| ISO | 2382 pt 19 | Analogue Computing |
| BS | 3527/19 | |

BS	4335	Glossary of terms used in project network analysis.
BS	5408	Glossary of documentation terms.
BS	6054	Glossary of terms for Micrographics.
BS	6135	Glossary of terms relating to the numerical control of machines.
ISO	3534	Statistics – vocabulary and symbols.
ISO	5127	Glossary of terms (various parts).
ISO	6760	Glossary of terms for documents and data elements in administration, commerce and industry.
IEC	271A	List of basic terms, definitions and related mathematics for reliability.
CCITT	Yellow Book	The ITU list of definitions of essential telecommunications terms.
CCITT	Orange Book (Vol 8)	As above for new data networks.

Note: Both ISO 2382 and BS 3527 are referred to collectively as 'Glossary of Terms Relating to Automatic Data Processing'

| CCITT V24 | List of definitions for interchange circuits between ter- |
| BS 4421 | minal equipment and data circuit-terminating equipment. |

| IEEE 696 | Microprocessor bus specification (S100). |

2. DATA REPRESENTATION AND CODES

| ANSI X3.4 | Code for Information Interchange. Defines ASCII, the American National Standard Code for Information Interchange. |
| ANSI X3.41 | Code extension techniques for use with 7-bit coded character set of American National Standard Code for Information Interchange. |

| BS 1991 | Letter symbols, signs and abbreviations. |
| BS 3763 | The International System of Units (SI). |

BS 4730	The United Kingdom 7-bit data code.
ISO 646	The basis for most data interchange standards.
ECMA 6	

BS 4730	The graphical representation of the control characters of the U.K. 7-bit data code
ISO 2047	
ECMA 17	

BS 4731	Rules for the derivation of 4-bit coded character sets.
ISO 963	
ECMA 14	

| BS 5716 | Codes for the representation of currencies and funds. |
| ISO 4217 | |

BS 6006	8-bit coded character set.
ISO 2047	
ECMA 17	

| ISO 2022 | Code extension technique for use with the U.K. 7-bit data code. Includes a compatible extension to 8-bits and the use of escape and shift characters for trans-formation between 7- and 8-bit code environments. |
| ECMA 35 | |

| EIA RS-244-B | Character code for numerical machine control perforated tape. |

| EIA RS-352 | One half inch magnetic tape reel for computer use (requirements for interchange). Specifies the essential physical dimensions. |

EIA	RS-358-B	Subset of American National Standard Code for Information Interchange for numerical machine control perforated tape.
ISO	2375	Procedure for registration of escape sequences.
ISO ECMA	6093 63	Representation of numerical values in character strings for information interchange.
ISO	6113	Bank telecommunications messages — attributes and characteristics.
ISO ECMA	6429 48	Additional control for character-imaging I/O devices. Covers the special control characters necessary for visual display and similar devices.
ISO	6523	Structure for identification of organisations for information interchange.
ISO	6936	Conversion between the ISO 7-bit coded character set (ISO 646) and the CCITT International Telegraph Alphabet No 2 (ITA). Specifies the rules for interworking between computer-based equipment and the international telex network. Relevant to teletex and videotex services.
ISO	6937 pt 1	Coded character sets for text communication — General Introduction.
ISO	6937 pt 2	Coded character sets for text communications — Latin alphabetic and non-alphabetic graphic characters.
ISO	6937 pt 3	Coded character sets for text communications — Control functions for document interchange.
ISO	7000	Graphic symbols — Index survey and compilation of the single sheets.
ISO	7064	Check character systems.
ISO	7341	Bases for nostro accounts reconciliation — Data elements required for interbank statements.
ISO	7350	Coded character sets for text communication — Procedures for registration of sub-repertoires of graphic characters.
ISO	7352	Organisation and representation of data elements for data interchange.
ISO	7372	Data elements used in trade.

Transliteration

BS	2979	Transliteration of (Slavic) Cyrillic and Greek characters
ISO	9 (Cyrillic)	into Latin characters.
ISO	843 (Greek)	Transliteration of Arabic characters into Latin characters
BS	4280	ters

BS	4812	Romanisation of Japanese.
ISO	259	Transliteration of Hebrew characters into Latin characters.
ISO	7098	Transliteration of Chinese characters into Latin characters.

3. MEDIA

BS	1808	Sizes and recommended layout of commercial forms —
ISO	216	letterheads and forms. Based on ISO 'A' series sizes (BS4000); includes invoices, etc.

BS	3880 pt 1	Paper tape for data processing — unpunched paper tape.
ISO	1729	Defines required properties of paper and dimensions of tape and spools.

BS	3880 pt 2	Dimensions and location of punched holes in paper tape;
ISO	1154	includes acceptable effects of humidity on tape.

BS	3880 pt 3	Representation of codes on paper tape. Implements
ISO	1113	BS 4730 (U.K. 7-bit code) and CCITT No 2 on paper tape.

BS	3880 pt 4	General requirements for data interchange on punched
ISO	2195	tape. Defines the requirements for handling and storage of tape.

BS	3968	
ISO	1861	7-track magnetic tape for data interchange recorded at
ISO	1864	200 rpi (bpi)
ISO	961	
ECMA	5	

BS	4503 pt 1	9-track magnatic tape for data interchange — recom-
ISO	1863	mended at 31.5 rpmm, NRZI; includes notes on
ISO	1864	transportation and spool specifications.
ISO	962	
ECMA	12	

BS	4503 pt 2	
ISO	3788	9-track magnetic tape for data interchange — recorded
ISO	1864	at 63 rpmm, phase encoded.
ISO	962	
ECMA	36	

BS	4636 pt 1	Unpunched paper cards. Properties and dimensions of
ISO	1681	cards together with storage recommendations.

BS	4636 pt 2	Dimensions and locations of rectangular holes in 12-row
ISO	1862	80-column punched cards.

BS	4732 pt 2	Magnetic tape labelling and file structure for data interchange — Part 2 label standards version 3. Defines a recording scheme for reading and interpreting tape labels on another computer.
ISO	1001	
ECMA	13	

BS	4783	Recommendations for the care and transportation of magnetic tape.

BS	4850 pt 1	Magnetic six-disc packs for data processing — mechanical and magnetic properties. Very detailed document.
ISO	2864 ·	
ECMA	32	

BS	4850 pt 2	Magnetic six-disc packs for data processing — track format; includes specifications for both control information and data.
ISO	3561	
ECMA	33	

BS	5079	Data interchange on 3.81 mm magnetic tape cassette phase encoded at 63 ft/min. Defines physical and magnetic properties of the tape, recording methods for 7- and 8-bit codes and cassette dimensions.
ISO	3407	
ISO	3275	
ECMA	34	

BS	5356 pt 1	Magnetic single-disc cartridge for data processing (top loaded) — mechanical and magnetic properties.
ISO	3562	
ECMA	38	

BS	5356 pt 2	Magnetic single-disc cartridge for data processing (top loaded) — track format.
ISO	3563	
ECMA	39	

BS	5359	Magnetic 11-disc packs for data processing — mechanical and magnetic properties.
ISO	3564	

BS	5537	Forms design sheet and layout chart.
ISO	3535	

BS	5595 pt 1	Interchangeable magnetic 12-disc pack with 100 Mbyte capacity. Comprehensive definition of physical and magnetic properties together with recording method and track layout.
ISO	4337	
ECMA	45	

BS	5595 pt 2	Interchangeable magnetic 12-disc pack with 200 Mbyte capacity. See BS 5595 pt 1.
ISO	5653	
ECMA	52	

BS	6003	Data interchange on 6.3mm magnetic tape cartridge 63 bpmm, phase encoded. Defines physical and magnetic properties together with track layout and recording format.
ISO	4057	
ECMA	46	

ECMA 62		Data interchange on 12.7 mm 9-track magnetic tape. Supersedes ECMA 12 and ECMA 36.
ISO	1862	9-track 200 rpi magnetic tape for information interchange.
ISO	1864	Unrecorded magnetic tape for information interchange — 200 and 800 rpi NRZI and 1600 rpi phase encoded. Physical and magnetic properties of unused magnetic tape.
ISO	3692	Reels and cores for 25.4 mm (1 inch) perforated paper tape.
ISO	5652	9-track magnetic tapes for data interchange — recorded at 246 cpmm, group coding.
ISO ECMA 54	5654 pt 1	200 mm flexible disc cartridges — mechanical and magnetic properties.
ISO ECMA 54	5654 pt 2	200 mm flexible disc cartridges — track format. This and ISO 5654 pt 1 define 'floppy discs' mechanically, magnetically and in layout together with storage containers.
ISO ECMA 56	6098	Self-loading cartridges for 12.7 mm wide magnetic tapes.
ISO	6586	Implementation of the ISO 7-bit and 8-bit coded character sets on punched cards. Based on ISO 1679 and ISO 2021 combined.
ISO ECMA 66	6596 pt 1	Data interchange on 130 mm (5.25 in) flexible disc cartridges, one-sided — mechanical and magnetic properties.
ISO ECMA 66	6596 pt 2	Data interchange on 130 mm (5.25 in) flexible disc cartridges, one-sided — track format.
ISO ECMA 58	6863	Flexible disc cartridge labelling and file structure for information interchange — for basic interchange on 200 mm discs.
ISO ECMA 59	7065 pt 1	200 mm flexible disc cartridges using modified fequency modulation on two sides — mechanical and magnetic properties.
ISO ECMA 59	7065 pt 2	200 mm flexible disc cartridges using modified frequency modulation on two sides — track format.
ISO ECMA 70	7487 pt 1	Data interchange on 130 mm flexible disc cartridges using MFM recording — mechanical and magnetic properties.

| ISO | 7487 pt 2 | Data interchange on 130 mm flexible disc cartridges |
| ECMA | 70 | using MFM recording — track format. |

| ISO | 7665 | Flexible disc cartridge labelling and file structure for |
| ECMA | 58 | information interchange — for basic and extended interchange on 130 mm and 200 mm discs. The definitive requirements for data interchange via floppy discs. |

MD — STD 10-011   80 column card files for information interchange.

4. INTERFACES

| BS | 4421 | A digital input interface for data collection systems. Although defined for data collection, may be used for peripheral connection. |

| BS | 6146 pt 1 | Interface system for programmable measuring apparatus — |
| IEC | 625 – 1 | functional, electrical and mechanical requirements. |

| BS | 6146 pt 2 | Interface system for programmable measuring apparatus |
| IEC | 625 – 2 | — code and format conventions. |

IEEE	696	Microprocessor bus (S100).
ISO	5656	Channel interface. Based on IBM practices and not likely to remain an international standard.
ISO	6548	Description of interface between process computing system and technical process.
ISO	6950	Point-to-point full duplex interface. A simple bi-directional interchange of 8 bits (extendable to 32) based on a French proposal.
ISO	6951	Processor system bus interface. Based on a 16-bit system originating from the U.K. MoD.
ISO	7068	Small computer to peripheral bus interface — data transfer between any two units. Based on the Univac D bus and providing 8 or 16 bits.

| ISO | 7069 | Small computer to peripheral bus interface — data transfer between computer and peripherals. Based on DIN 66 202 and providing 8-bit transfer. |

5. MISCELLANEOUS EQUIPMENT

| BS | 2481 | Layout of printing and function keys on typewriters. |

| BS | 4822 | Keyboard arrangements for data processing — the graphic |
| ISO | 2530 | characters of the U.K. 7-bit data code. Does not specify function key layout. |

| BS | 5231 | Principles governing the positioning of control keys on |
| ISO | 3244 | keyboards of data processing equipment. |

BS	5464 pt 1	Optical character recognition − character set OCR−A
ISO	1073 pt 1	− shapes and dimensions and the printed image.
ECMA	8	

BS	5464 pt 2	Optical character recognition − character set OCR−B
ISO	1073 pt 2	− shapes and dimensions of the printed image.
ECMA	11	

| BS | 5644 | Computer output microfiche (COM) − A6 size. |

| BS | 5959 | Office machine keyboards − key numbering systems and |
| ISO | 4169 | layout charts. |

| BS | 6462 | Modification of keyboards to include symbols for SI units. |

| ECMA | 23 | Keyboards generating the code combinations of the characters of the ECMA 7-bit character set. |

| ECMA | 30 | OCR−B subsets for numeric applications. |

| ECMA | 42 | Alphanumeric character set for 7×9 matrix printers. Defines the shape of 73 graphic characters designed for OCR applications. |

| ECMA | 51 | Implementation of the numeric OCR−A font with 9×9 matrix printers. |

| ISO | 1831 | Printing specification for optical character recognition |
| ECMA | 15 | (OCR). |

| ISO | 2126 | Basic arrangements for alphanumeric keyboards operated with both hands. |

| ISO | 3243 | Keyboards for countries whose languages have alphabetic extenders. |

INTERNATIONAL STANDARDS RELEVANT TO DATA TRANSMISSION

1. MISCELLANEOUS

| ANSI | X3.1 | Synchronous signalling rates for data transmission. Defines preferred signalling rates for voice grade channels. |

ANSI	X3.15	Bit sequencing of the American National Standard Code for Information Interchange in serial bit-by-bit data transmission. Refers to ASCII (X3.4) and defines the serial numbering of bits.
ANSI	X3.24	Signal quality at interface between data terminal equipment and synchronous data communication equipment for serial data transmission. Equivalent to RS–334–A.
ANSI	X3.25	Character structure and character parity sense for parallel-by-bit communication in the American National Standard Code for Information Interchange.
ANSI	X3.28	Procedures for the use of communication control characters of American National Standard Code for Information Interchange in specified data communication links. Defines ASCII communication control characters (ACK, NAK, etc.)
ANSI	X3.36	Synchronous high-speed data signalling rates between data terminal equipment and data communication equipment. Defines preferred signalling rates for systems transmitting at rates higher than those commonly used in voice grade channels.
ANSI	X3.44	Determination of the performance of data communication systems.
ANSI	X3.57	Structure for formatting message headings for information interchange using the American National Standard Code for Information Interchange for data communication system control. Specifies message heading formats for ASCII based systems.
ANSI	X3.79	Determination of performance of data communication systems that use bit-oriented control procedures.

BS	4505 pt 1	Digital data transmission − basic mode control procedures. Uses transmission control characters excluded from text; see also pt 4.
ISO	1745	
ECMA	16	

BS	4505 pt 2	Digital data transmission − character structure for start/stop and synchronous transmission. Defines sense of bits, parity bit and start and stop elements.
ISO	1177	
CCITT	V4	

BS	4505 pt 3	Digital data transmission − the use of longitudinal parity for error detection. The use of a single parity character at the end of a data block.
ISO	1155	

BS	4505 pt 4	Digital data transmission − code independent information transfer. An extension of BS 4505 pt 1 to permit transmission without regard to bit patterns.
ISO	2111	
ECMA	24	

BS	4505 pt 5	Assignment of connector pin numbers for interchange circuits between data terminal equipment and data
ISO	2110	

communications equipment (25-pin connectors). This relates the V24 circuit numbers to pin-numbers of the 25-way D connector used for modems and other equipment specified by CCITT recommendations V21, V23, V25, V26 amongst others.

BS	4505 pt 6	Digital data transmission — recovery, abort and interrupt
ISO	2628	procedures. Defines the procedures to be imple-
ECMA	26, 27, 28	mented when a data link fails or when transmission
		is to be terminated abnormally.

BS	4505 pt 7	Digital data transmission — conversational information
ISO	2629	message transfer. The procedures for reversal of
ECMA	29	the master/slave roles.

BS	4505 pt 8	37-pin and 9-pin DTE/DCE interface connectors and pin
ISO	4902	assignments.

BS	4505 pt 9	15-pin DTE/DCE interface connector and pin assign-
ISO	4903	ments.

BS	5203	Determination of performance of an information path within a data communication system.

BS	5397 pt 1	High-level data link control procedures — frame struc-
ISO	3309	ture. The basic frame within which HDLC data are
ECMA	40	transmitted. HDLC provides for synchronous, bit-oriented, code-independent, and interactive transmissions with greater error protection and freedom than basic mode.

BS	5397 pt 2	High-level data link control procedures — elements of
ISO	4335	procedures. Defines the arrangement of commands,
ECMA	49	responses and supervisory signals and their numbering to control the flow of information in a data link.

BS	5397 pt 3	High-level data link control procedures — unbalanced
ISO	6159	class of procedures. The simplest HDLC system with a single master computer communicating with one or more terminals.

BS	5397 pt 4	High-level data link control procedures — balanced class
ISO	6256	of procedures. An HDLC link with two computers interworking. Equivalent to and compatible with CCITT X25 link access protocol.
CCITT	F200	Teletex service. The basic characteristics and operating procedures only of the service are described.
CCITT	S15	Use of the Telex network for data transmission at 50 baud.

CCITT	S16	Connection to the Telex network of an automatic terminal via a V24 interface.
CCITT	S17	Calling and answering with automatic terminal equipment on the Telex network.
CCITT ISO	S18 6936	Conversion between International Alphabet No 2 and International Alphabet No 5. Enables Teletex to interwork with the Telex network.
CCITT	S30	Standardisation of basic page-printing machines using International Alphabet No 5.
CCITT	S31	Transmission characteristics at the interface between DTE and DCE when using a 200 baud stop/start terminal in accordance with International Alphabet No 5.
CCITT	S32	Answer-back units for 200 baud start/stop terminals using International Alphabet No 5.
CCITT	S33	Standardisation of a text for the measurement of the margin of start/stop terminals using International Alphabet No 5.
CCITT	S60	Terminal equipment for use in the Teletex service. Detailed technical specifications for terminal equipment.
CCITT	S61	Character repertoire and coded character sets for the international Teletex service. Defines the 8-bit Teletex code which is a subset of ISO 6937.
CCITT	S62	Control procedures for the Teletex service. Defines the protocols for message interchange. Uses X21 and X25.
CCITT	S70	Network independent basic transport service for Teletex. The OSI transport layer for Teletex.
CCITT	S100	International information interchange for interactive videotex. The requirements for the international exchange of videotex (eg Prestel) data base information.
CCITT	V1	Equivalence between binary notation signals and the significant conditions of a two-condition code. Relates binary 0 and 1 to the various modulation methods and holes in paper tape. Used with V28 defines voltage polarity and on-off conditions.
CCITT	V2	Power levels for data transmission over telephone lines.
CCITT ISO	V3 646	International Alphabet No 5.
CCITT	V4	General structure of signals of International Alphabet No 5 for data transmission over public telephone networks.
CCITT	V5	Standardisation of modulation rates and data signalling rates for synchronous data transmission in the

		general switched telephone network. Preferred rates give transmission speeds of 600, 1200 and 2400 bits per second.
CCITT	V6	Standardisation of modulation rates and data signalling rates for synchronous data transmission on leased telephone type circuits. Preferred rates give transmission speeds up to 9600 bits per second.
CCITT	V10	Electrical characteristics for unbalanced double-current interchange circuits for general use with integrated circuit equipment in the field of data communications. See also X26.
CCITT	V11	Electrical characteristics for balanced double-current interchange circuits for general use with integrated circuit equipment in the field of data communications. See also X27.
CCITT	V13	Answerback unit simulator.
CCITT	V15	Use of acoustic coupling of data transmission.
CCITT	V16	Recommendations for modems for transmission of medical analogue data. Provides for the transmission of three simultaneous signals over the switched telephone network.
CCITT	V19	Modems for parallel data transmission using telephone signalling frequencies. Using the frequencies of a mf (push button) keyphone provides transmission speed up to 10 characters per second.
CCITT	V20	Parallel data transmission modems standardised for universal use in the general switched network.
CCITT	V21	200 baud modem standardised for use in the general switched network.
CCITT	V22	1200 bits per second full duplex 2-wire modem standardised for use in the general switched telephone network.
CCITT	V23	600/1200 baud modem standardised for use in the general switched telephone network.
CCITT	V24	List of definitions for interchange circuits between data terminal equipment and data circuit-terminating equipment. The signals and operating procedures across a defined interface. Can also provide physical demarcation. See also BS 4421 and V28.
CCITT	V25	Automatic calling and/or answering equipment on the general switched telephone network. Defines the conditions and procedures.
CCITT	V26	2400 bits per second modem standardised for use in the general switched telephone network.
CCITT	V26 bis	2400/1200 bits per second modem standardised for use in the general switched telephone network. Provides 2400 bits per second as V26 with 1200 bits per second fallback together with a 75 bits per second backward channel.

CCITT V27	4800 bits per second modem with manual equalizer standardised for use on leased telephone-type circuits. Provides full or half duplex synchronous transmission with an optional 75 bits per second backward channel.
CCITT V27 bis	4800 bits per second modem with automatic equalizer standardised for use on leased telephone-type circuits. Provides full or half duplex synchronous transmission using differential 8-phase modulation.
CCITT V27 ter	4800/2400 bits per second modem standardised for use in the general switched telephone network. Provides full or half duplex synchronous transmission using differential 8-phase modulation with an adaptive equalizer.
CCITT V28	Electrical characteristics for unbalanced double-current interchange circuits. The electrical conditions previously in V24 and suitable for transmission speeds up to 20 kilobits per second.
CCITT V29	9600 bits per second modem standardised for use on leased telephone-type circuits. Full or half duplex synchronous transmission with fallback speeds of 7200 and 4800 bits per second.
CCITT V31	Electrical characteristics for single-current interchange circuits controlled by contact closure. Provides for transmission speeds up to 75 bits per second.
CCITT V35	Data transmission at 48 kilobits per second using 60–108 kHz group band circuits.
CCITT V36	Modems for synchronous data transmission using 60–108 kHz group band circuits.
CCITT V40	Error indication with electro-mechanical equipment.
CCITT V41	Code-independent error control system. Defines the use of a polynomial block check character.
CCITT V50	Standard limits for transmission quality of data transmission.
CCITT V51	Organisation of the maintenance of international telephone-type circuits used for data transmission.
CCITT V52	Characteristics of distortion and error-rate measuring apparatus for data transmission.
CCITT V53	Limits for the maintenance of telephone-type circuits used for data transmission.
CCITT V54	Loop test device for modems. Defines a user modem and circuit tester.
CCITT V55	Impulsive noise measurement instrument for data transmission.
CCITT V56	Comparative tests of modems for use over telephone-type circuits.
CCITT V57	Comprehensive data test set for high transmission rates. Defines a test set capable of operating in the range 20-48 kilobits per second for use with modems based on V35.

EIA RS-232-C   Interface between data terminal equipment and data communication equipment employing serial binary data interchange.

Defines electrical signal characteristics, mechanical characteristics and functional description of the interchange circuits of a standard interface.

The US equivalent of V24.

EIA RS-269-B   Synchronous signalling rates for data transmission.

Specifies signalling rates at the DTE/DCE interface for equipment operating over 4 kHz channels.

EIA RS-328   Message facsimile equipment for operation on switched voice facilities using data communication and terminal equipment.

EIA RS-334   Signal quality at interface between data processing terminal equipment and synchronous data communication equipment for serial data transmission.

Defines the data and timing signals that flow across RS-232-C interfaces. Same as ANSI X3.24.

EIA RS-357   Interface between facsimile terminal equipment and voice frequency data communication terminal equipment.

Defines, for analogue facsimile machines based on RS-328, the exchange of control signals and analogue data signals.

EIA RS-363   Standard for specifying signal quality for transmitting and receiving data processing terminal equipments using serial data transmission at the interface with non-synchronous data communication equipment.

Specifies signal quality for start/stop (asynchronous) terminals operating across an RS-232-C interface.

EIA RS-366-A   Interface between data terminal equipment and automatic calling equipment for data communication.

Defines electrical signal characteristics, interface mechanical characteristics, and functional description of interchange circuits on the interface.

EIA RS-373   Unattended operation of facsimile equipment (as defined in EIA Standard RS-328).

Specifies the interface requirements and control signal sequence between RS-328 type facsimile equipment and telephone facilities.

EIA RS-404   Standard for start/stop signal quality between data terminal equipment and non-synchronous data communication equipment.

Defines the signal quality for signals across an RS-232-C interface between start/stop terminals and non-synchronous processing equipment.

EIA RS-408   Interface between numerical control equipment and data terminal equipment employing parallel binary data interchange.

EIA RS-449   General purpose 37-position and 9-position interface for

	data terminal equipment and data circuit-terminating equipment employing serial binary data interchange.
	U.S. equivalent of BS 4505 parts 8 and 9 (ISO 4902 and 4903).
EIA RS–499–1	Addendum No. 1 to RS–449. Redefines New Signal (circuit NS) in line with international practice.
ISO 2593	34-pin DTE/DCE interface connector and pin assignments.
	Physical and electrical properties for the interface to high speed modems to CCITT V35.
ISO 7477	Requirements for DTE to DCE physical connection using 15 and 37 pin connectors.
FED–STD–1001	Telecommunications: Synchronous high speed data signalling rates between data terminal equipment and data communication equipment.
FED–STD–1005	Telecommunications: Coding and modulation requirements for non-diversity 2400 bit/second modems.
FED–STD–1006	Telecommunications: Coding and modulation requirements for 4800 bit/second modems.
FED–STD–1007	Telecommunications: Coding and modulation requirements for duplex 9600 bit/second modems.
FED–STD–1008	Telecommunications: Coding and modulation requirements for duplex 600 and 1200 bit/second modems.
FED–STD–1010	Telecommunications: Bit sequencing of the American National Standard Code for Information Interchange in serial-by-bit data transmission.
FED–STD–1011	Telecommunications: Character structure and character parity sense for serial-by-bit data communication in the American National Standard Code for Information Interchange.
FED–STD–1012	Telecommunications: Character structure and character parity sense for parallel-by-bit data communication in the American National Standard Code for Information Interchange.
FED–STD–1013	Telecommunications: Synchronous signalling rates between data terminal equipment and data circuit-terminating equipment utilising 4 kHz circuits.
FED–STD–1020A	Telecommunications: Electrical characteristics of balanced voltage digital interface circuits.
FED–STD–1030A	Telecommunications: Electrical characteristics of unbalanced voltage digital interface circuits.
FED–STD–1031	Telecommunications: General purpose 37-position and 9-position interface for data terminal equipment and data circuit-terminating equipment.

2. CONNECTIONS TO BRITISH TELECOM

| BS   6301 | Saftey requirements for apparatus for connection to B.T. networks. |

BS	6305	General requirements for apparatus for connection to the Public Switched Telephone Network run by B.T.
BS	6320	Modems for connection to the B.T. Public Switched Telephone Network.
BS	6328	Apparatus for connection of private circuits to B.T. circuits.

3. PUBLIC DATA NETWORKS

CCITT X1   User classes of service for public data networks.

The defined classes are as follows: (classes 1 through 7 use International Alphabet No. 5 for address selection and service signals):

Class	Speed	Mode
1	300	Start/stop
2	50–200	Start/stop
3	600	Synchronous
4	2400	Synchronous
5	4800	Synchronous
6	9600	Synchronous
7	48 000	Synchronous
8	2400	Packet
9	4800	Packet
10	9600	Packet
11	48 000	Packet

CCITT X2   Recommended user facilities available in public data networks.

Defines a range of obligatory, recommended and optional user facilities.

CCITT X3   Packet assembly-disassembly facility (PAD) in a public data network.

CCITT X4   General structure of signals of International Alphabet No. 5 code for data transmission over public data networks.

CCITT X20   Interface between data terminal equipment and data circuit-terminating equipment for start-stop services in user classes 1 and 2 on public data networks.

A 4-circuit interface for simple character-oriented terminal devices. Defines the circuits, interface procedures and protocol requirements.

CCITT X20 bis   V21–compatible interface between DTE and DCE for start-stop transmission services on public data networks.

Enables existing character-oriented terminal equipment to connect to new public data networks.

CCITT X21   Interface between data terminal equipment and data circuit-terminating equipment for synchronous operation on public data networks.

An 8-circuit interface for terminals in user classes 3 through 6. Defines the circuits, and the interchange signalling sequences. Lists the countries proposing to provide byte timing.

CCITT X21 bis   The use on public data networks of data terminal equipment designed for interfacing to synchronous V-series modems.

CCITT X22   Multiplex DTE/DCE interface for user classes 3 through 6 on public data networks.

CCITT X24   List of definitions for interchange circuits for data terminal equipment and data circuit-terminating equipment on public data networks. The public data network equivalent of V24 and designed to provide effective interface specifications.

CCITT X25   Interface between data terminal equipment and data circuit-terminating equipment in the packet mode on public data networks.

The specification for the operation of packet switched data networks. In three levels:

Level 1 – equipment connection based on X21.

Level 2 – the link access protocol or procedures for the terminal to communicate with the network local exchange. Equivalent to the HDLC scheme of ISO 3309, 4335 and 6356.

Level 3 – packet formats and the rules associated with their use.

CCITT X26   Electrical characteristics for unbalanced double-current interchange circuits for general use with integrated circuit equipment in the field of data communications. Defines the nature of the electrical signals at interfaces when used with integrated circuits.

(Formerly V10)

CCITT X27   Electrical characteristics for balanced double-current interchange circuits for general use with integrated circuit equipment in the field of data communications.

Defines the nature of the electrical signals at interfaces when used with integrated circuits.

(Formerly V11)

CCITT X28   DTE/DCE interface for a start/stop mode data terminal equipment accessing the packet assembly/disassembly facility (PAD) in a public data network situated in the same country.

CCITT X29   Procedures for the exchange of control information and user data between a packet mode DTE and a packet assembly/disassembly facility (PAD). Together

		with X28 and X3 this defines a higher level than X25 whereby terminals may send/receive character strings to/from a network, these being assembled/disassembled by a facility of an exchange in the network.
CCITT	X40	Standardisation of frequency shift modulated transmission systems for the provision of telegraph and data channels by frequency division of a primary group.
CCITT	X50	Fundamental parameters of a multiplexing scheme for the international interface between synchronous data networks.
		Defines a method of transmission between international data networks at 64 kilobits per second using frames of 2+6 bits grouped into three 8-bit byte quarters.
CCITT	X50 bis	Fundamental parameters of a 48 kilobit per second user data signalling rate transmission scheme for the international interface between synchronous data networks.
CCITT	X51	Fundamental parameters of a multiplexing scheme for the international interface between synchronous data networks using 10-bit envelope structure.
CCITT	X51 bis	Fundamental parameters of a 48 kilobits per second user data signalling rate transmission scheme for the international interface between synchronous data networks using 10-bit envelope structure.
CCITT	X52	Method of encoding anisochronous signals into a synchronous user bearer.
CCITT	X53	Numbering of channels on international multiplexed links at 64 kilobits per second.
CCITT	X54	Allocation of channels on international multiplexed links at 64 kilobits per second.
CCITT	X60	Common channel signalling for circuit switched data applications.
CCITT	X61	Signalling system number 7-data user part. This was formerly CCITT X60.
CCITT	X70	Terminal and transit control signalling system for start-stop services on international circuits between anisochronous data networks.
		Defines the signalling schemes to establish and close down calls between subscriber of user classes 1 and 2.
CCITT	X71	Decentralised terminal and transit control signalling system on international circuits between synchronous data networks.
CCITT	X75	Terminal and transit call control procedures and data transfer system on international circuits between packet-switched data networks.

CCITT	X80	Interworking of inter-exchange signalling systems for circuit switched data services.
CCITT	X87	Principles and procedures for realisation of international user facilities and network utilities in public data networks.
CCITT	X92	Hypothetical reference connection for public synchronous data networks.
CCITT	X95	Network parameters in public data networks.
CCITT	X96	Call progress signals in public data networks.
CCITT	X110	Routing principles for international public data services through switched public data networks of the same type.
CCITT	X121	International numbering plan for public data networks.
CCITT	X130	Provisional objectives for call set-up and clear-down times in public synchronous data networks (circuit switching).
CCITT	X132	Provisional objectives for grade of service in international data communications over circuit switched public data networks.
CCITT	X150	DTE and DCE test loops for public data networks.
CCITT	X180	Administrative arrangements for international Closed User Groups (CUG).
CCITT	X200	OSI Reference model. (See also ISO 7498).
ECMA	37	Digital data transmission — supplementary transmission control functions.
ECMA	71	HDLC recommended procedures. Defines a restricted range of HDLC procedures aiming to reduce system complexity.
ECMA	72	Transport protocol. Part of the OSI procedures.
ECMA	75	Session protocol. Part of the OSI procedures.
FED–STD–1003A		Telecommunications: Synchronous bit-oriented data link control procedure. (Advanced Data Communications Control Procedures).
ISO	7478	High-level data link control procedures — multi-link control procedures.
		Part of the data link layer of the Open System Interconnection (OSI) model defining the means of accepting data from the transport layer, scheduling them for transmission over a multiplicity of data links and reassembling them on receipt.
ISO	7480	Start/stop transmission signal quality at DTE/DCE interfaces.
ISO	7498	OSI — basic reference level.
		Defines the basic 7-layer reference model for open system interconnection. It is intended that this will form the foundation upon which will be built the architecture of completed OSI systems and into which all other OSI standards will fit.
		The 7-layer reference model is illustrated elsewhere (page 31).

ISO   7776   Standardisation of the X.25 DTE link layer procedure.
ISO   7777   Frame structure for non-centralised multiple access data
                      communication systems.

STANDARDS RELEVANT TO COMPUTING, BY CATEGORY

Note: multiple entries on one line indicate equivalents.

1. Glossaries/definitions

    BS 3527
    BS 4335
    BS 5408
    BS 6054, ISO 6196
    BS 6135, ISO 2806
    CCITT V24
    EIA RS–232–C
    IEC 271A
    ISO 3534
    ISO 5127
    ISO 6760

2. Banking

    ISO 6113
    ISO 7341

3. Character Codes

    ANSI X3.4
    BS 4730, ISO 646, ECMA 6, CCITT V3
    BS 4731, ISO 963, ECMA 14
    BS 6006, ISO 4873, ECMA 43
    ISO 2022, ECMA 35
    ISO 2375
    ISO 6429, ECMA 48
    ISO 6936
    ISO 6937
    ISO 7000
    ISO 7350

4. Data Representation

    ANSI X3.41
    ANSI X3.92
    BS 1991
    BS 3763
    BS 5716, ISO 4217
    ISO 6093, ECMA 63
    ISO 6523
    ISO 6760

ISO 7064
ISO 7352
ISO 7372

5. Document Printing

BS 1808, ISO 216
BS 5537, ISO 3535

6. Interfaces

BS 4421
BS 6146, IEC 625–1
IEEE 696
ISO 5656
ISO 6548
ISO 6950
ISO 6951
ISO 7068
ISO 7069

7. Keyboard Layouts

BS 2481, ISO 1091
BS 4822, ISO 2530
BS 5231, ISO 3244
BS 5959, ISO 4169
BS 6462
ECMA 23
ISO 2126
ISO 3243

8. Magnetic Discs

BS 4850, ECMA 32, ISO 2864
BS 5359, ISO 3564
BS 5356, ECMA 38, ECMA 39, ISO 3562, ISO 3563
BS 5595, ECMA 45, ECMA 52, ISO 4337, ISO 5653
ECMA 69
ECMA 73, ISO 7297
ISO 5654, ECMA 54
ISO 6596, ECMA 66
ISO 6863, ECMA 58
ISO 6901
ISO 6902
ISO 7065, ECMA 59
ISO 7665, ECMA 58, ECMA 67

9. Magnetic Tapes

BS 3968

BS 4503, ISO 1863, ISO 1864, ISO 962, ECMA 12, ECMA 36
BS 4732, ISO 1001, ECMA 13
BS 4783
BS 5079, ECMA 34, ISO 3407, ISO 3275
BS 6003, ECMA 46, ISO 4057
ECMA 62
ISO 1862
ISO 1864
ISO 6098, ECMA 56

10. Microfilm (COM)

BS 5644, ISO 5126
BS 6054, ISO 6196

11. OCR

BS 5464, ECMA 8, ECMA 11, ISO 1073
ECMA 30
ECMA 42
ECMA 51
ISO 1831, ECMA 15

12. Punched Cards and Tape

BS 3692
BS 3880, ISO 1113, ISO 1154, ISO 1729, ISO 2195
BS 4636, ISO 1681, ISO 1682
ISO 6586
MD–STD 10 – 011

13. Transliteration

BS 2979, ISO 9, ISO 843
BS 4280, ISO 213
BS 4812, ISO 3602
ISO 259
ISO 7098

STANDARDS RELEVANT TO DATA TRANSMISSION, BY CATEGORY

1. General

ANSI X3.1
ANSI X3.15
ANSI X3.25
ANSI X3.28
ANSI X3.36
BS 4505, CCITT V4, ISO 1155, ISO 1177
BS 5203

CCITT S15
CCITT S16
CCITT S17
CCITT V1
CCITT V2
CCITT V3, ISO 646
CCITT V5
CCITT V6
CCITT V40
CCITT V41
CCITT Yellow Book
CCITT Orange Book
EIA RS–269–B
FED–STD–1001
FED–STD–1010
FED–STD–1011
FED–STD–1012
FED–STD–1013

2. Basic Mode Procedures

BS 4505 (1), ECMA 16, ISO 1745
BS 4505 (4), ECMA 24, ISO 2111
BS 4505 (6), ECMA 26, ECMA 27, ECMA 28, ISO 2628
BS 4505 (7), ECMA 29, ISO 2629
ECMA 37

3. BT Connections

BS 6328
BS 6305
BS 6320
BS 6301

4. HDLC Procedures

BS 5397 (1), ECMA 40, ISO 3309
BS 5397 (2), ECMA 49, ISO 4335
BS 5397 (3), ISO 6159
BS 5397 (4), ISO 6256
ECMA 71
FED–STD–1003A
ISO 7478
ISO 7777

5. Interfaces and Connectors

BS 4505 (5), ISO 2110
BS 4505 (8), ISO 4902
BS 4505 (9), ISO 4903
CCITT V24
CCITT V28

CCITT V31
CCITT X26
CCITT X27
EIA RS–232–C
EIA RS–357
EIA RS–366–A
EIA RS–408
EIA RS–449
EIA RS–449–1
FED–STD–1020A
FED–STD–1030A
FED–STD–1031
ISO 2593
ISO 7477
ISO 7480

6. Modems

CCITT V15
CCITT V16
CCITT V19
CCITT V20
CCITT V21
CCITT V23
CCITT V25
CCITT V26
CCITT V27
CCITT V29
CCITT V35
CCITT V36
FED–STD–1005
FED–STD–1006
FED–STD–1007
FED–STD–1008

7. Open Systems Interconnection (OSI)

CCITT X200
ISO 7498
ECMA 72
ECMA 75

8. Public Data Networks

CCITT X1
CCITT X2
CCITT X3
CCITT X20
CCITT X21
CCITT X22
CCITT X24

```
CCITT  X25
CCITT  X28
CCITT  X29
CCITT  X40
CCITT  X50
CCITT  X51
CCITT  X52
CCITT  X53
CCITT  X54
CCITT  X60
CCITT  X61
CCITT  X70
CCITT  X71
CCITT  X75
CCITT  X80
CCITT  X87
CCITT  X92
CCITT  X96
CCITT  X110
CCITT  X121
CCITT  X131
CCITT  X132
CCITT  X150
CCITT  X180
ISO    7776
```

9. Test and Measurement

```
ANSI   X3.24
ANSI   X3.44
CCITT  V50
CCITT  V51
CCITT  V52
CCITT  V54
CCITT  V55
CCITT  V56
CCITT  V57
```

10. Text Communication

```
CCITT  F200
CCITT  S18
CCITT  S60
CCITT  S61
CCITT  S62
CCITT  S70
CCITT  S100
```

SOME COMMON INTERFACES

Connectors with 9, 15, 25 and 37 pins are used between various types of transmission equipment, depending on the standards to which that equipment is working.

The various circuits or signals that can be carried over these interfaces are defined in CCITT and EIA (RS) standards and, although given different designations, are functionally equivalent.

The physical construction of the interface connectors is defined by ISO and by EIA (RS). These are identical and therefore shown only once.

The assignment of interchange circuits to pin numbers is defined by ISO and EIA (RS) and these are functionally equivalent although using different nomenclature.

INTERCHANGE CIRCUITS

INTERCHANGE CIRCUITS (V24)

Circuit number	Description
102	Signal ground or common return
103	Transmitted data
104	Received data
105	Request to send
106	Ready for sending
107	Data set ready
108/1	Connect data set to line
108/2	Data terminal ready
109	Data channel received line signal detector
110	Data signal quality detector
111	Data signalling rate selector (DTE source)
113	Transmitter signal element timing (DTE source)
114	Transmitter signal element timing (DCE source)
115	Receiver signal element timing (DCE source)
116	Select standby
118	Transmitted backward channel data
119	Received backward channel data
120	Transmit backward channel line signal
121	Backward channel ready
122	Backward channel received line signal detector
124	Select frequency groups
125	Calling indicator
126	Select transmit frequency
129	Request to receive
130	Transmit backward tone
131	Received character timing
132	Return to non-data mode
140	Remote loopback for point to point circuits
141	Local loopback

142	Test indicator
191	Transmitted voice answer
192	Received voice answer
201	Signal ground or common return
202	Call request
203	Data line occupied
204	Distant station connected
205	Abandon call
206	Digit signal (2^0)
207	Digit signal (2^1)
208	Digit signal (2^2)
209	Digit signal (2^3)
210	Present next digit
211	Digit present
213	Power indication
G	Signal ground or common return
T	Transmit
R	Receive

INTERCHANGE CIRCUITS (RS 232)

INTERCHANGE CIRCUIT	DESCRIPTION	Gnd	Data		Control		Timing	
			From DCE	To DCE	From DCE	To DCE	From DCE	To DCE
AA	Protective Ground	X						
AB	Signal Ground/Common Return	X						
BA	Transmitted Data			X				
BB	Received Data		X					
CA	Request to Send					X		
CB	Clear to Send				X			
CC	Data Set Ready				X			
CD	Data Terminal Ready					X		
CE	Ring Indicator				X			
CF	Received Line Signal Detecctor				X			
CG	Signal Quality Detector				X			
CH	Data Signal Rate Selector (DTE)					X		
CI	Data Signal Rate Selector (DCE)				X			
DA	Transmitter Signal Element Timing (DTE)							X
DB	Transmitter Signal Element Timing (DCE)						X	
DD	Receiver Signal Element Timing (DCE)						X	
SBA	Secondary Transmitted Data			X				
SBB	Secondary Received Data		X					
SCA	Secondary Request to Send					X		
SCB	Secondary Clear to Send				X			
SCF	Secondary Received Line Signal Detector				X			

LIST OF INTERCHANGE CIRCUITS (ISO 4903)

CIRCUIT DESIGNATION	DESCRIPTION
G	Signal ground or common return
Ga	DTE common return
Gb	DCE common return
T	Transmit
R	Receive
C	Control
I	Indication
S	Signal element timing
B	Byte timing
F	Frame start identification

INTERCHANGE CIRCUITS (RS 449)

CIRCUIT MNEMONIC	CIRCUIT NAME	CIRCUIT DIRECTION	CIRCUIT TYPE	
SG	Signal Ground	—		
SC	Send Common	to DCE	Common	
RC	Receive Common	from DCE		
IS	Terminal in Service	to DCE		
IC	Incoming Call	from DCE	Control	
TR	Terminal Ready	to DCE		
DM	Data Mode	from DCE		
SD	Send Data	to DCE	Data	PRIMARY CHANNEL
RD	Receive Data	from DCE		
TT	Terminal Timing	to DCE		
ST	Send Timing	from DCE	Timing	
RT	Receive Timing	from DCE		
RS	Request to Send	to DCE		
CS	Clear to Send	from DCE		
RR	Receiver Ready	from DCE		
SQ	Signal Quality	from DCE	Control	
NS	New Signal	to DCE		
SF	Select Frequency	to DCE		
SR	Signalling Rate Selector	to DCE		
SI	Signalling Rate Indicator	from DCE		
SSD	Secondary Send Data	to DCE	Data	SECONDARY CHANNEL
SRD	Secondary Receive Data	from DCE		
SRS	Secondary Request to Send	to DCE		
SCS	Secondary Clear to Send	from DCE	Control	
SRR	Secondary Receiver Ready	from DCE		
LL	Local Loopback	to DCE		
RL	Remote Loopback	to DCE	Control	
TM	Test Mode	from DCE		
SS	Select Standby	to DCE	Control	
SB	Standby Indicator	from DCE		

EQUIVALENCY TABLE

	RS-449		RS-232C		CCITT Recommendation V24
SG	Signal Ground	AB	Signal Ground	102	Signal Ground
SC	Send Common			102a	DTE Common
RC	Receive Common			102b	DCE Common
IS	Terminal in Service				
IC	Incoming Call	CE	Ring Indicator	125	Calling Indicator
TR	Terminal Ready	CD	Data Terminal Ready	108/2	Data Terminal Ready
DM	Data Mode	CC	Data Set Ready	107	Data Set Ready
SD	Send Data	BA	Transmitted Data	103	Transmitted Data
RD	Receive Data	BB	Receive Data	104	Received Data
TT	Terminal Timing	DA	Transmitter Signal Element Timing (DTE Source)	113	Transmitter Signal Element Timing (DTE Source)
ST	Send Timing	DB	Transmitter Signal Element Timing (DCE Source)	114	Transmitter Signal Element Timing (DCE Source)
RT	Receive Timing	DD	Receiver Signal Element Timing	115	Receiver Signal Element Timing (DCE Source)
RS	Request to Send	CA	Request to Send	105	Request to Send
CS	Clear to Send	CB	Clear to Send	106	Ready for Sending
RR	Receiver Ready	CF	Received Line Signal Detector	109	Data Channel Received Line Signal Detector

EQUIVLAENCY TABLE *CONTD.*

RS-449		RS-232C		CCITT Recommendation V24	
SQ	Signal Quality	CG	Signal Quality Detector	110	Data Signal Quality Detector
NS	New Signal				
SF	Select Frequency			126	Select Transmit Frequency
SR	Signalling Rate Selector	CH	Data Signal Rate Selector (DTE Source)	111	Data Signalling Rate Selector (DTE Source)
SI	Signalling Rate Indicator	CI	Data Signal Rate Selector (DCE Source)	112	Data Signalling Rate Selector (DCE Source)
SSD	Secondary Send Data	SBA	Secondary Transmitted Data	118	Transmitted Backward Channel Data
SRD	Secondary Receive Data	SBB	Secondary Received Data	119	Received Backward Channel Data
SRS	Secondary Request to Send	SGA	Secondary Request to Send	120	Transmit Backward Channel Line Signal
SCS	Secondary Clear to Send	SCB	Secondary Clear to Send	121	Backward Channel Ready
SRR	Secondary Receiver Ready	SCF	Secondary Received Line Signal Detector	122	Backward Channel Received Line Signal Detector
LL	Local Loopback			141	Local Loopback
RL	Remote Loopback			140	Remote Loopback
TM	Test Mode			143	Test Indicator
SS	Select Standby			116	Select Standby
SB	Standby Indicator			117	Standby Indictor

INTERFACE CIRCUITS

INTERFACE CONNECTOR PIN ASSIGNEMENTS (RS 232)

PIN NUMBER	CIRCUIT	DESCRIPTION
1	AA	Protective Ground
2	BA	Transmitted Data
3	BB	Received Data
4	CA	Request to Send
5	CB	Clear to Send
6	CC	Data Set Ready
7	AB	Signal Ground (Common Return)
8	CF	Received Line Signal Detector
9	−	(Reserved for Data Set Testing)
10	−	(Reserved for Data Set Testing)
11		Unassigned
12	SCF	Secondary Received Line Signal Detector
13	SCB	Secondary Clear to Send
14	SBA	Secondary Transmitted Data
15	DB	Transmission Signal Element Timing (DCE Source)
16	SBB	Secondary Received Data
17	DD	Receiver Signal Element Timing (DCE Source)
18		Unassigned
19	SCA	Secondary Request to Send
20	CD	Data Terminal Ready
21	CG	Signal Quality Detector
22	CE	Ring Indicator
23	CH/CI	Data Signal Rate Selector (DTE/DCE Source)
24	DA	Transmitted Signal Element Timing (DTE Source)
25		Unassigned

V24 INTERFACE CIRCUITS (100 SERIES)

102   − Signal Ground: signal common return, may be connected to protective earth.

103   − Transmitted Data.

104   − Received Data.

105   − RTS (Request to Send): When ON causes the DCE to assume the transmit mode.

106   − Ready for Sending: When ON indicates that the DCE is conditioned for the transmission of data.

107   − DSR (Data Set Ready): When ON indicates that the DCE is ready to exchange further control signals with the DTE (can be taken to indicate that DCE is on-line).

108/1   − CDSL (Connect Data Set to Line): When ON causes the DCE to connect signal conversion or other equipment to line.

108/2   − DTR (Data Terminal Ready): When ON indicates that the DTE is ready to operate.

109 — Received Line Signal Receiver: When ON indicates that the received signal is within the specified limits.

110 — Data Signal Quality Detector: When ON indicates that the received data is believed to be correct.

111 — Signalling Rate Selector (DTE): When On selects the higher of two available transmission rates.

112 — Signalling Rate Selector (DCE): When ON selects the higher of two available transmission rates.

113 — Transmitter Timing (DTE): Provides a clock train at the modulation rate.

114 — Transmitter Timing (DCE): Provides a clock train at the modulation rate.

115 — Receiver Timing (DCE): Provides a clock train at the modulation rate.

116 — Select Standby: When ON selects the standby mode of operation.

117 — Standby Indicator: When ON indicates that the DCE is able to operate in standby mode.

118 — Transmitted Backward Channel

119 — Received Backward Channel

120 — Transmit Backward Channel Line Signal: When ON causes the DCE to enter the backward channel transmit mode.

121 — Backward Channel Ready: When ON indicates that the DCE is conditioned to transmit on a backward channel.

122 — Backward Channel Received Line Signal Detector: When ON indicates that the backward channel received signal is within specified limits.

123 — Backward Channel Signal Quality Detector: When ON indicates that the received backward channel data is believed to be correct.

124 — Select Frequency Groups: Used to select alternative frequency groups for data representation.

125 — Calling Indicator: When ON indicates that a switched network call is being received.

126 — Select Transmit Frequency: When ON selects the higher transmit frequency.

127 — Select Receive Frequency: When ON selects the lower receive frequency.

128 — Receiver Timing (DTE): Provides a clock train at the modulation rate.

129 — Request to Receive: When ON causes the DCE to assume the receive mode.

130 — Transmit Backward Tone: When ON causes the DCE to transmit a tone on the backward channel.

131 — Received Character Timing: Provides the DTE with character timing as specified.

132 — Return to Non-Data Mode: When ON causes the DCE to revert to non-data mode without releasing any line connection.

133 — Ready for Receiving: When ON indicates that the DTE is capable of accepting data.

134 — Received Data Present: When ON indicates data that represents information (rather than supervisory messages).

142 — Test Indicator: When ON indicates that the DCE is in test mode (and precluding transmission of data to a remote DTE).

V24 INTERFACE CIRCUITS (200 SERIES)

Automatic Calling

Circuit No	Function	From DCE	To DCE
201	Signal ground	X	X
202	Call request		X
203	Data line occupied	X	
204	Distant station connected	X	
205	Abandon call	X	
206	Digit signal (2^0)		X
207	Digit signal (2^1)		X
208	Digit signal (2^2)		X
209	Digit signal (2^3)		X
210	Present next digit	X	
211	Digit present		X
213	Power indication	X	

191 — Transmitted Voice Answer
192 — Received Voice Answer.
201 — Signal Ground: Signal common return, may be connected to protective earth.
202 — Call Request: when ON requests the automatic calling equipment to originate a call.
203 — Data Line Occupied: when ON indicates that the communications channel is in use.
204 — Distant Station Connected: when ON indicates receipt of connection signal from the remote DCE.
205 — Abandon Call: when ON indicates that the call should be abandoned.
206 — Digit Signal (2^0) ⎫
207 — Digit Signal (2^1) ⎪ indicates successive digits to be called
208 — Digit Signal (2^2) ⎬ in binary notation
209 — Digit Signal (2^3) ⎭
210 — Present Next Digit: when ON indicates that the automatic calling equipment is ready to accept the next digit.
211 — Digit Present: when ON causes the automatic calling equipment to read the next digit.
213 — Power indication: when ON indicates that power is available to the automatic calling equipment.

ASSINGMENT OF PIN NUMBERS

PIN assignments for 25-Pin Connector (ISO 2110)

PIN NUMBER	INTERCHANGE CIRCUIT NUMBERS				
	Voice Band Modems				
	Asynchronous		Synchronous	Parallel	
	V21	V23	V26 V26 bis V27 V27 bis	V19 V20 Instation	V20 Outstation
1	Note 1	Note 1	Note 1	Note 1	Note 1
2	103	103	103	Note 5	192–A
3	104	104	104	A1	A1
4	105	105	105	A2	A2
5	106	106	106	A3	A3
6	107	107	107	A4	B1
7	102	102	102	131	B2
8	109	109	109	109	B3
9	N	N	N	C1	C1
10	N	N	N	C2	C2
11	126	N	N	C3	C3
12	F	122	122	C4	192–B
13	F	121	121	B1	Return
14	F	118	118	B2	125–A
15	F	Note 2	114	B3	125–B
16	F	119	119	B4	105–A
17	F	Note 2	115	191–A	105–B
18	141	141	141	191–B	129–A
19	F	120	120	130	129–B
20	108*	108*	108*	105	119–A
21	140	140	140	125	119–B
22	125	125	125	108*	107–A
23	N	111	111	107	107–B
24	N	N	113	102	108–A
25	142	142	142	124	108–B
Electrical Characteristics	V28	V28	V28	V28	V31

* 108/1 or 108/2

Note 1, 2, 5: *see Notes on page 159*

INTERCHANGE CIRCUIT NUMBERS					
Public Data Networks		Telegraph		Automatic Calling	
X20 bis	X21 bis	Telex	Other	Telephone V25	Telex S16
Note 1	Note 1	Note 1	Note 1	Note 1	Note 1
103	103	103	103	211	211
104	104	104	104	205	205
F	105	N	N	202	202
106	106	106	106	210	210
107	107	107	107	213	213
102	102	102	102	201	201
109	109	109	109	F	F
N	N	N	N	N	N
N	N	N	N	N	N
F	N	N	N	F	F
F	F	F	F	F	F
F	F	F	F	204	204
F	F	F	F	206	206
F	114	F	F	207	207
F	F	F	F	208	208
F	115	F	F	209	209
N	N	132	F	F	F
F	F	F	F	F	F
108*	108*	108/2	108/2	F	F
N	N	F	F	F	F
125	125	125	125	203	203
N	N	N	N	N	N
N	F	N	N	N	N
N	142	F	F	F	F
V28	V28	V28	V28	V28	V28

ISO 2110

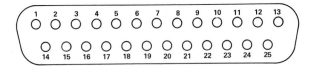

**DTE connector face
contact numbering**

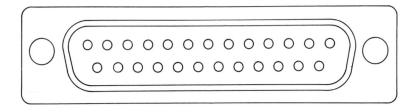

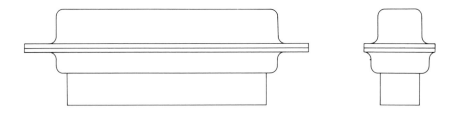

DTE interface connector

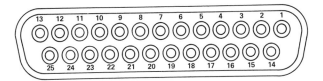

**DCE connector face
contact numbering**

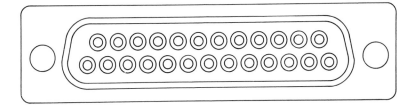

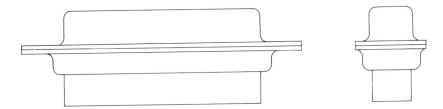

DCE interface connector

PIN ASSIGNMENTS FOR 9-PIN CONNECTOR

FIRST SEGMENT ASSIGNMENT		SECOND SEGMENT ASSIGNMENT		DIRECTION TO	
PIN NUMBER	CIRCUIT NUMBER	PIN NUMBER	CIRCUIT NUMBER	DTE	DCE
1	Note 1				
2	122	6	102b	X	
3	118	7	120		X
4	119	8	121	X	
5	102	9	102a		X

See Notes on page 159.

PIN ASSIGNMENTS FOR 9-POSITION CONNECTOR (RS 449)

FIRST SEGMENT ASSIGNMENT		SECOND SEGMENT ASSIGNMENT		DIRECTION	
CONTACT NUMBER	CIRCUIT	CONTACT NUMBER	CIRCUIT	TO DCE	FROM DCE
1	Shield				
2	SRR	6	RC		X
3	SSD	7	SRS	X	
4	SRD	8	SCS		X
5	SG	9	SC	X	

ISO 4902

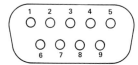

**DTE connector face
contact numbering**

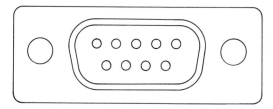

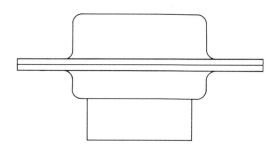

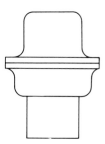

DTE 9-pin interface connector

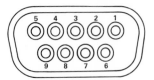

**DCE connector face
contact numbering**

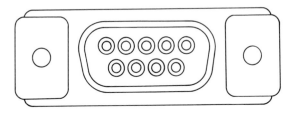

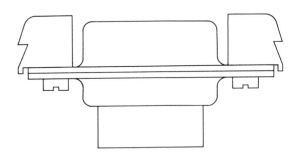
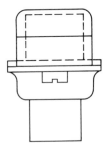

DCE 9-pin interface connector

PIN ASSIGNMENTS FOR 37-PIN CONNECTOR (ISO 4902)

FIRST SEGMENT ASSIGNMENT		SECOND SEGMENT ASSIGNMENT		DIRECTION TO	
PIN NUMBER	CIRCUIT NUMBER	PIN NUMBER	CIRCUIT NUMBER	DTE	DCE
1	Note 1			—	—
2	N	20	102b	X	
3	N	21	N		
4	103	22	103		X
5	114	23	114	X	
6	104	24	104	X	
7	105	25	105		X
8	115	26	115	X	
9	106	27	106	X	
10	141	28	N		X
11	107	29	107	X	
12	108*	30	108*		X
13	109	31	109	X	
14	140	32	N		X
15	125	33	N	X	
16	111 or 126	34	N		X
17	113	35	113		X
18	142	36	N	X	
19	102	37	102a		X

* 108/1 or 108/2
See Notes on p. 159

ASSIGNMENTS FOR 37-POSITION CONNECTOR (RS 449)

FIRST SEGMENT ASSIGNMENT		SECOND SEGMENT ASSIGNMENT		DIRECTION	
CONTACT NUMBER	CIRCUIT	CONTACT NUMBER	CIRCUIT	TO DCE	FROM DCE
1	Shield				
2	SI	20	RC		X
3	Spare	21	Spare		
4	SD	22	SD	X	
5	ST	23	ST		X
6	RD	24	RD		X
7	RS	25	RS	X	
8	RT	26	RT		X
9	CS	27	CS		X
10	LL	28	IS	X	
11	DM	29	DM		X
12	TR	30	TR	X	
13	RR	31	RR		X
14	RL	32	SS	X	
15	IC	33	SQ		X
16	SF/SR	34	NS	X	
17	TT	35	TT	X	
18	TM	36	SB		X
19	SG	37	SC	X	

ISO 4902

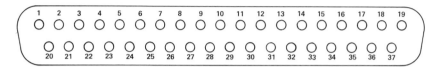

**DTE connector face
contact numbering**

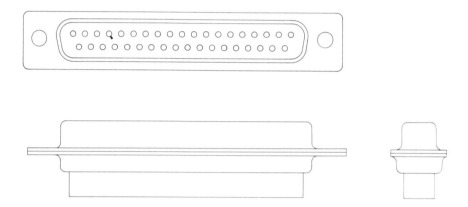

DTE 37-pin interface connector

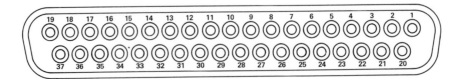

**DCE connector face
contact numbering**

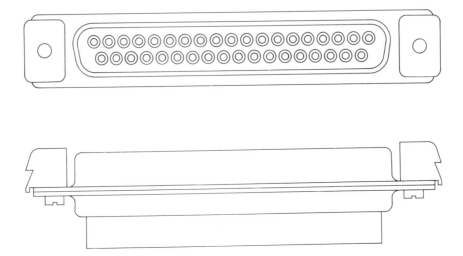

DCE 37-pin interface connector

ISO 4903

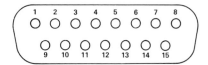

**DTE connector face
contact numbering**

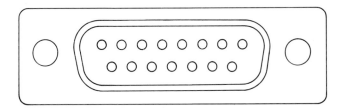

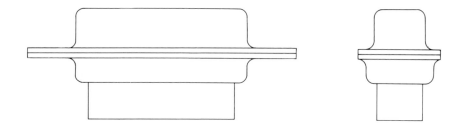

DTE interface connector

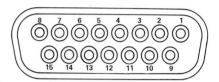

**DCE connector face
contact numbering**

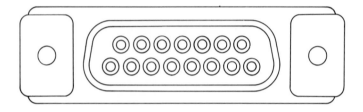

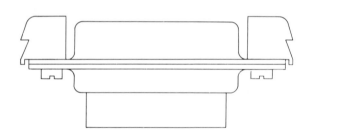
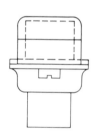

DCE interface connector

PIN ASSIGNMENTS FOR INTERFACE CCITT
RECOMMENDATIONS X20, X21 AND X22 (ISO 4903)

PIN NUMBER	INTERCHANGE CIRCUIT ASSIGNMENT				
	X20		X21		X22
	X26	X27	X26	X27	X27
1	Note 1	Note 1	Note 1	Note 1	Note 1
2	T	T(A)	T	T(A)	T(A)
3	–	–	C	C(A)	C(A)
4	R	R(A)	R(A)	R(A)	R(A)
5	–	–	I(A)	I(A)	I(A)
6	–	–	S(A)	S(A)	S(A)
7	–	–	B(A)	B(A)	F(A)
8	G	G	G	G	G
9	Ga	T(B)	Ga	T(B)	T(B)
10	–	–	Ga	C(B)	C(B)
11	Gb	R(B)	R(B)	R(B)	R(B)
12	–	–	I(B)	I(B)	I(B)
13	–.	–	S(B)	S(B)	S(B)
14	–	–	B(B)	B(B)	F(B)
15	Reserved for future international use				

Where balanced circuits are concerned, the associated pairs are designated 'A' and 'B' (CCITT X27).
See Notes below.

Notes

1. Pin 1 is assigned for connecting the shields between tandem sections of shielded cables. May be connected to protective ground or signal ground.

2. Where signal element timing is provided in the DCE, pin 15 will be used for circuit 114 and pin 17 for circuit 115.

N   Reserved for national use.

F   Reserved for future use.

*   108/1 or 108/2

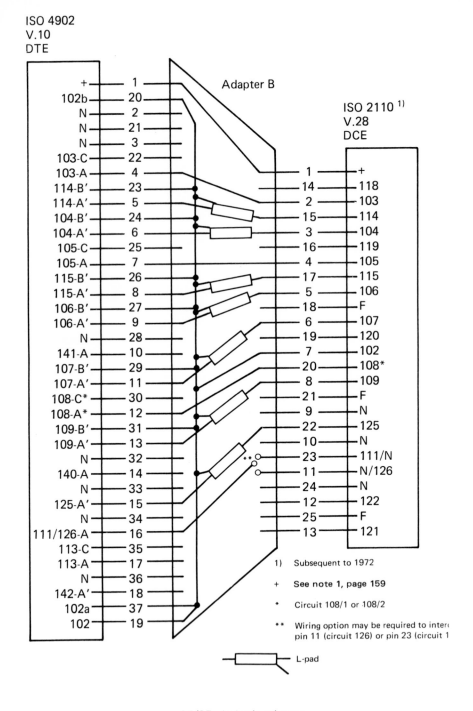

ISO 4902
V.10
DTE

Adapter B

ISO 2110 [1)]
V.28
DCE

+	1					
102b	20					
N	2					
N	21					
N	3					
103-C	22					
103-A	4		1		+	
114-B'	23		14		118	
114-A'	5		2		103	
104-B'	24		15		114	
104-A'	6		3		104	
105-C	25		16		119	
105-A	7		4		105	
115-B'	26		17		115	
115-A'	8		5		106	
106-B'	27		18		F	
106-A'	9		6		107	
N	28		19		120	
141-A	10		7		102	
107-B'	29		20		108*	
107-A'	11		8		109	
108-C*	30		21		F	
108-A*	12		9		N	
109-B'	31		22		125	
109-A'	13		10		N	
N	32		23		111/N	
140-A	14		11		N/126	
N	33		24		N	
125-A'	15		12		122	
N	34		25		F	
111/126-A	16		13		121	
113-C	35					
113-A	17					
N	36					
142-A'	18					
102a	37					
102	19					

1)   Subsequent to 1972

+   See note 1, page 159

*   Circuit 108/1 or 108/2

**   Wiring option may be required to inter(
     pin 11 (circuit 126) or pin 23 (circuit 1

L-pad

37/25-pin basic adapter

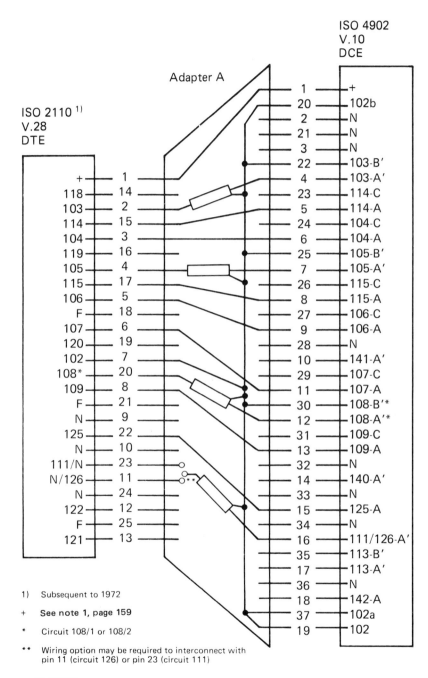

ISO 4902
V.10
DCE

Adapter A

ISO 2110 [1]
V.28
DTE

1) Subsequent to 1972

+ See note 1, page 159

* Circuit 108/1 or 108/2

** Wiring option may be required to interconnect with
pin 11 (circuit 126) or pin 23 (circuit 111)

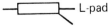 L-pad

25/37-pin basic adapter

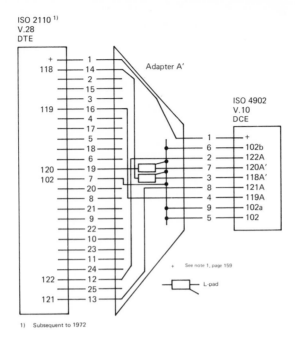

9/25-pin optional companion adapter

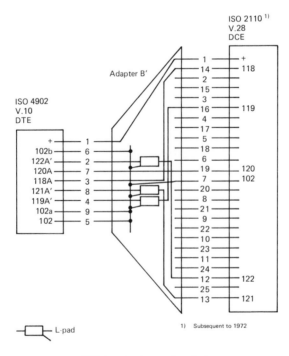

9/25-pin optional companion adapter

IEEE 488 INTERFACE FOR PROGRAMMABLE
INSTRUMENTATION CONTACT ASSIGNMENT FOR
24-WAY CONNECTOR

CONTACT	SIGNAL	MNEMONIC
1	Digital Input/Output 1	DIO1
2	Digital Input/Output 2	DIO2
3	Digital Input/Output 3	DIO3
4	Digital Input/Output 4	DIO4
5	End of Identity	EOI
6	Data Valid	DAV
7	Not ready for Data	NRFD
8	Not Data Accepted	NDAC
9	Interface Clear	IFC
10	Service Request	SRQ
11	Attention	ATN
12	Shield	SHIELD
13	Digital Input/Output 5	DIO5
14	Digital Input/Output 6	DIO6
15	Digital Input/Output 7	DIO7
16	Digital Input/Output 8	DIO8
17	Remote Enable	REN
18	Ground Return (6)	GND (6)
19	Ground Return (7)	GND (7)
20	Ground Return (8)	GND (8)
21	Ground Return (9)	GND (9)
22	Ground Return (10)	GND (10)
23	Ground Return (11)	GND (11)
24	Ground Return Logic	GND LOGIC

Notes:
The ground return contacts are referenced to signal contacts as indicated by the parenthesised numbers. EOI and REN use contact 24 for ground return.

IEEE 696 (S100) MICROPROCESSOR BUS

Pin No	Mnemonic	Function
1	+8V (B)	power
2	+16V (B)	power
3	XRDY (S)	ready (1 of 2 see 72)
4	$\overline{V}_{10}$ (S)	
5	$\overline{V}_{11}$ (S)	
6	$\overline{V}_{12}$ (S)	
7	$\overline{V}_{13}$ (S)	vectored input
8	$\overline{V}_{14}$ (S)	lines 0 to 7
9	$\overline{V}_{15}$ (S)	
10	$\overline{V}_{16}$ (S)	
11	$\overline{V}_{17}$ (S)	
12	$\overline{\text{NMI}}$ (S)	non maskable interrupt

13	$\overline{\text{PWRFAIL}}$ (B)	power fail signal
14	$\overline{\text{TMA}}_3$ (M)	temporary master priority bit 3
15	A_{18} (M)	extended address bit 18
16	A_{16} (M)	extended address bit 16
17	A_{17} (M)	extended address bit 17
18	$\overline{\text{SDSB}}$ (M)	disable 8 status signals
19	$\overline{\text{CDSB}}$ (M)	disable 5 control output
20	OV (B)	common with pin 100
21	NDEF	not defined
22	$\overline{\text{ADSB}}$ (M)	disable address
23	$\overline{\text{DODSB}}$ (M)	disable data output
24	$\emptyset$ (B)	master bus timing
25	p $\overline{\text{STVAL}}$ (M)	status valid stroke
26	pHLDA (M)	coordinates bus transfer with HOLD
27	RFU	reserved for future use
28	RFU	reserved for future use
29	A_5 (M)	address bit 5
30	A_4 (M)	address bit 4
31	A_3 (M)	address bit 3
32	A_{15} (M)	address bit 15
33	A_{12} (M)	address bit 12
34	A_9 (M)	address bit 9
35	DO_1 (M)	data out bit 1
36	DO_0 (M)	data out bit 0
37	A_{10} (M)	address bit 10
38	DO_4 (M)	data out bit 4
39	DO_5 (M)	data out bit 5
40	DO_6 (M)	data out bit 6
41	DI_2 (S)	data in bit 2
42	DI_3 (S)	data in bit 3
43	DI_7 (S)	data in bit 7
44	sM1 (M)	op-code fetch cycle flag
45	sOUT (M)	data transfer to output cycle flag
46	sINP (M)	data transfer from input cycle flag
47	sMEMR (M)	data transfer from memory cycle flag
48	sHLTA (M)	acknowledge HALT instruction exe-cuted
49	CLOCK (B)	2mHz ($\pm 0.5\%$)
50	OV (B)	common with pin 100
51	+8V (B)	common with pin 1
52	-16V (B)	power
53	OV (B)	common with pin 100
54	SLAVE $\overline{\text{CLR}}$ (B)	reset bus slaves
55	$\overline{\text{TMA0}}$ (M)	temporary master priority bit 0
56	$\overline{\text{TMA1}}$ (M)	temporary master priority bit 1
57	$\overline{\text{TMA2}}$ (M)	temporary master priority bit 2
58	sXTRQ (M)	requests 16 bit slaves to assert SIXTN
59	$\overline{\text{SIXTN}}$ (M)	16 bit slave response to sXTRQ
61	A_{20} (M)	extended adddress bit 20
62	A_{21} (M)	extended address bit 21

63	A_{22} (M)	extended address bit 22
64	A_{23} (M)	extended address bit 23
65	NDEF	not defined
66	NDEF	not defined
67	$\overline{\text{PHANTOM}}$ (M/S)	disable slave & enable phantom slave
68	MWRT (B)	equal to $(\overline{\text{pWR-sOUT}})$
69	RFU	reserved for future use
70	OV (B)	common with pin 100
71	RFU	reserved for future use
72	RDY (S)	see pin 3
73	$\overline{\text{INT}}$ (S)	primary interrupt request
74	$\overline{\text{HOLD}}$ (M)	coordinates bus transfers with pHLDA
75	$\overline{\text{RESET}}$ (B)	reset bus master devices
76	pSYNC (M)	identifies BS 1
77	pWR (M)	valid data on DO bus
78	pDBIN (M)	requests data on DI bus
79	A_0 (M)	address bit 0
80	A_1 (M)	address bit 1
81	A_2 (M)	address bit 2
82	A_6 (M)	address bit 6
83	A_7 (M)	address bit 7
84	A_8 (M)	address bit 8
85	A_{13} (M)	address bit 13
86	A_{14} (M)	address bit 14
87	A_{11} (M)	address bit 11
88	DO_2 (M)	data out bit 2
89	DO_3 (M)	data out bit 3
90	DO_7 (M)	data out bit 7
91	DI_4 (M)	data in bit 4
92	DI_5 (M)	data in bit 5
93	DI_6 (M)	data in bit 6
94	DI_1 (M)	data in bit 1
95	DI_0 (M)	data in bit 0
96	sINTA (M)	identifies bus input cycles following INT
97	$\overline{\text{sWO}}$ (M)	data transfer from M to S cycle flag
98	$\overline{\text{ERROR}}$ (S)	error during present cycle
99	$\overline{\text{POC}}$ (B)	power on clear (low for 10 ms)
100	OV (B)	system ground

Notes

B = Backblame

S = Slave

M = Master

Signals DO_0 through DO_7 may also be used as ED_0 through ED_7 (bidirectional even data bits).

Signals DI_0 through DI_7 may also be used as OD_0 through OD_7 (bidirectional odd data bits).

FACSIMILE STANDARDS

CCITT GROUP 1

Index of co-operation	264 (176 optional)
Transmission time for A4 document	6 minutes
Scanning density	3.85 lines per mm
Scanning line frequency	180 lines per minute (240 optional)
Modulation (leased circuits only)	Amplitude black as higher carrier between 1300/1900 Hz
(leased or switched)	frequency black as $f_0 + 400$ Hz white as $f_0 - 400$ Hz f_0 as 1700 Hz

CCITT GROUP 2

Index of co-operation	264
Transmission time for A4 document	3 minutes
Scanning density	3.85 lines per mm
Scanning line frequency	360 lines per minute (300 optional)
Modulation	Vestigial sideband amplitude black as minimum white as maximum carrier as 2100 Hz

CCITT GROUP 3

Transmission time for A4 document	30 seconds
Scanning density	3.85 lines per mm (7.7 lines per mm optional)
Modulation	Digital 2400 bits/s or 4800 bits/s

7 Materials

WAVEGUIDE SIZES

Frequency (GHz)	Wavelength (cm)	WG Internal dimensions (in.)	WG Internal dimensions (cm)	RCSC British WG No	British Inter-Services Ref. No. Brass 70/30	British Inter-Services Ref. No. Aluminium	EIA WR ( )	IEC R ( )	NATO NWG (1 or 2)*	JAN Type RG ( ) Copper or brass	JAN Type RG ( ) Aluminium	JAN Type RG ( ) Silver	Cut-off Frequency
0.32- 0.49	93.68-61.18	23.80 × 11.5	58.420 × 29.210	00			2300	3	01				0.265
0.35- 0.53	85.65-56.56	21.0 × 10.5	53.34 × 26.670	0			2100	4	02				0.281
0.41- 0.625	73.11-47.96	18.0 × 9.0	45.72 × 22.86	1			1800	5	03		201		0.328
0.49- 0.75	61.18-39.97	15.0 × 7.5	38.1 × 19.65	2			1500	6	04		202		0.393
0.64- 0.96	46.84-31.23	11.5 × 5.75	29.210 × 14.605	3			1150	8	05		203		0.513
0.75- 1.12	39.95-26.76	9.75 × 4.875	24.765 × 12.3825	4			975	9	06		204		0.605
0.96- 1.45	31.23-20.67	7.7 × 3.85	19.558 × 9.779	5			770	12	07		205		0.766
1.12- 1.70	26.76-17.63	6.5 × 3.25	16.510 × 8.255	6		012-0037	650	14	08	69	103		0.908
1.45- 2.20	20.67-13.62	5.1 × 2.55	12.954 × 6.477	7			510	18	09				1.157
1.70- 2.60	17.63-11.53	4.3 × 2.15	10.922 × 5.461	8	083-0144	083-0144	430	22	10	104	105		1.372
2.20- 3.30	13.63- 9.08	3.4 × 1.7	8.636 × 4.318	9A	012-0040	012-0042	340	26	11	112	113		1.763
2.60- 3.95	11.53- 7.59	2.84 × 1.34	7.2163 × 3.403	10	083-0068	083-0069	284	32	12	48	75		2.078
3.30- 4.90	9.08- 6.12	2.29 × 1.145	5.8166 × 2.909	11A	012-0045	012-0047	229	40	13				2.577
3.95- 5.85	7.95- 5.12	1.872 × 0.872	4.7549 × 2.2149	12	083-0077	083-0078	187	48	14	49	95		3.152
4.90- 7.05	6.12- 4.25	1.59 × 0.795	4.0486 × 2.0193	13	083-0146	083-0147	159	58	15				3.711
5.85- 8.20	5.12- 3.66	1.372 × 0.622	3.4849 × 1.58	14	083-0081	083-0082	137	70	16	50	106		4.301
7.05-10.00	4.25- 2.99	1.222 × 0.497	2.880 × 1.2624	15	083-0086	083-0087	112	84	17	51	68		5.259
8.20-12.40	3.66- 2.42	0.90 × 0.40	2.286 × 1.016	16	083-0097	083-0099	90	100	18	52	67		6.557

Frequency (GHz)	Wavelength (cm)	WG Internal dimensions (in.)	WG Internal dimensions (cm)	RCSC British WG No	British Inter-Services Ref. No. Brass 70/30	British Inter-Services Ref. No. Aluminium	EIA WR ( )	IEC R ( )	NATO NWG (1 or 2)*	JAN Type RG ( ) Copper or brass	JAN Type RG ( ) Aluminium	JAN Type RG ( ) Silver	JAN Type RG ( ) Aluminium	JAN Type RG ( ) Silver	Cut-off Frequency
10.00– 15.00	2.99– 2.00	0.75 × 0.375	1.9050 × 0.9525	17			75	120	19						2.868
12.40– 18.00	2.42– 1.66	0.622 × 0.311	1.58 × 0.790	18	083-0101		62	140	20	91		107			9.426
15.00– 22.00	2.00– 1.36	0.510 × 0.255	1.295 × 0.6477	19			51	180	21						11.574
18.00– 26.50	1.66– 1.13	0.420 × 0.170	1.0668 × 0.4318	20	Precision		42	220	22	53	121	66			14.047
22.00– 33.00	1.36– 0.91	0.340 × 0.170	0.8636 × 0.4318	21			34	260	23						17.328
26.50– 40.00	1.13– 0.75	0.280 × 0.140	0.7112 × 0.3556	22	083-1500		28	320	24			96			21.081
33.00– 50.00	0.91– 0.60	0.224 × 0.112	0.5659 × 0.2845	23	083-1501		22	400	25			97			26.342
40.00– 60.00	0.75– 0.50	0.188 × 0.94	0.4775 × 0.2388	24	083-1502		19	500	26						31.357
50.00– 75.00	0.60– 0.40	0.148 × 0.074	0.3759 × 0.1880	25	083-1503		15	620	27			98			39.863
60.00– 90.00	0.50– 0.33	0.122 × 0.061	0.3098 × 0.1550	26	083-1504		12	740	28			99			48.350
75.00–100.00	0.40– 0.27	0.100 × 0.050	0.2540 × 0.1270	27	083-1505		10	900	29						59.010
90.00–140.00	0.33– 0.22	0.080 × 0.040	0.2032 × 0.1016	28	083-1506		8	1200	30						73.80
140.00–220.00	0.22– 0.14	0.051 × 0.025	0.1295 × 0.0635												116.80

* N.B. (1) Aluminium.   (2) Copper based alloy.

The cut-off wavelength of a rectangular waveguide, the wide dimension of which is a cm is given by $\lambda_{co} = 2a$

For a waveguide $\dfrac{1}{\lambda^2} + \dfrac{1}{\lambda_{co}^2} = \dfrac{1}{\lambda_o^2}$

where λ = waveguide wavelength, λ_{co} = waveguide cut-off wavelength, and λ_o = free space wavelength.

BRITISH STANDARD COPPER WIRE TABLE

S.W.G.	Diameter (inches)	Resistance (a)	Length (b)	Current rating (c)	Turns per linear inch					Turns per square inch					Nearest American wire gauge
					Enamel	Single silk	Double silk	Single cotton	Double cotton	Enamel	Single silk	Double silk	Single cotton	Double cotton	
10	0.128	1.866	6.67	15.442	7.48	–	–	7.35	7.0	56	–	–	54	49	10
12	0.104	2.826	10.23	10.194	9.09	–	–	8.8	8.4	82.6	–	–	77.4	70.6	12
14	0.080	7.776	17.16	6.032	11.78	–	–	11.2	10.5	139	–	–	125.4	110	14
16	0.064	7.463	26.86	3.86	14.8	14.7	14.5	13.9	12.0	219	216	210	193.2	169	16
18	0.048	13.27	47.66	2.1715	19.7	19.8	19.4	18.0	16.8	388	392	376	324	282	19
20	0.036	23.59	85.00	1.2215	26.0	26.0	25.3	23.5	21.0	676	676	640	552	441	21
22	0.028	38.99	140.6	0.73	33.0	33.0	31.9	29.1	25.4	1089	1089	1081	847	645	23
24	0.022	63.16	228.3	0.4561	41.6	42.1	40.0	36.7	31.0	1731	1772	1600	1347	961	25
26	0.018	94.4	340.0	0.3054	50.2	51.2	48.3	43.0	35.4	2520	2621	2333	1849	1253	27
28	0.0148	139.6	503.0	0.2064	61.0	61.7	57.4	50.2	38.6	3721	3807	3295	2520	1490	28
30	0.0124	199	716.6	0.1450	72.5	72.4	66.6	57.1	44.4	5256	5242	4436	3260	1971	29
32	0.0108	262	943.3	0.1099	82.7	81.9	74.6	62.8	47.8	6839	6708	5565	3944	2285	31
34	0.0092	361	1300	0.0798	97	94.3	84.7	69.9	51.7	9409	8892	7174	4886	2673	32
36	0.0076	529	1903	0.0545	116	111	97.9	85.4	59.9	13456	12321	9584	7293	3588	34
38	0.0060	849	3056	0.0340	145	135	113	99	67.7	21025	18225	12769	9801	4583	36
40	0.0048	1327	4766	0.0217	178	161	131	112	75.1	31684	25921	17161	12544	5640	38

(a) Ohms per 1000 yards at 60°F; (b) Yards per lb; (c) Amps at 1200 amps per square inch.

R.F. CABLES (BRITISH UR SERIES)

UR No.	Nominal Impedance Z_0 (ohms)	Overall diameter –inches	Inner conductor –inches	Capacity pF/ft.	Maximum Operating voltage R.M.S.	Approx. Attenuation dB per 100 ft.				Approx. RG equivalent
						10 MHz	100 MHz	300 MHz	1000 MHz	
43	52	0.195	0.032	29	2750	1.3	4.3	8.7	18.1	58/U
57	75	0.405	0.044	20.6	5000	0.6	1.9	3.5	7.1	11A/U
63*	75	0.855	0.175	14	4400	0.15	0.5	0.9	1.7	
67	50	0.405	7/0.029	30	4800	0.6	2.0	3.7	7.5	213/U
74	51	0.870	0.188	30.7	15000	0.3	1.0	1.9	4.2	218/U
76	51	0.195	19/0.0066	29	1800	1.6	5.3	9.6	22.0	58C/U
77	75	0.870	0.104	20.5	12500	0.3	1.0	1.9	4.2	164/U
79*	50	0.855	0.265	21	6000	0.16	0.5	0.9	1.8	
83*	50	0.555	0.168	21	2600	0.25	0.8	1.5	2.8	
85*	75	0.555	0.109	14	2600	0.2	0.7	1.3	2.5	
90	75	0.242	0.022	20	2500	1.1	3.5	6.3	12.3	59B/U

All the above cables have solid dielectric with a velocity factor of 0.66 with the exception of those marked with an asterisk, which are helical membrane and have a velocity factor of 0.96.

R.F. CABLES (U.S.A. RG SERIES)

Cable No.	Nominal Impedance Z_0 (ohms)	Cable Outside Diameter	Velocity Factor	Approximate Attenuation (dB per 100 ft.)					Capacity pF/ft.	Maximum Operating Voltage RMS
				1 MHz	10 MhZ	10 MHz	1000 MHz	3000 MHz		
RG-5/U	52.5	0.332 in.	0.659	0.21	0.77	2.9	11.5	22.0	28.5	3000
RG-5B/U	50.0	0.332 in.	0.659	0.16	0.66	2.4	8.8	16.7	29.5	3000
RG-6A/U	75.0	0.332 in.	0.659	0.21	0.78	2.9	11.2	21.0	20.0	2700
RG-8A/U	50.0	0.405 in.	0.659	0.16	0.55	2.0	8.0	16.5	30.5	4000
RG-9/U	51.0	0.420 in.	0.659	0.16	0.57	2.0	7.3	15.5	30.0	4000
RG-9B/U	50.0	0.425 in.	0.659	0.175	0.61	2.1	9.0	18.0	30.5	4000
RG-10A/U	50.0	0.475 in.	0.659	0.16	0.55	2.0	8.0	16.5	30.5	4000
RG-11A/U	75.0	0.405 in.	0.66	0.18	0.7	2.3	7.8	16.5	20.5	5000
RG-12A/U	75.0	0.475 in.	0.659	0.18	0.66	2.3	8.0	16.5	20.5	4000
RG-13A/U	75.0	0.425	0.659	0.18	0.66	2.3	8.0	16.5	20.5	4000
RG-14A/U	50.0	0.545	0.659	0.12	0.41	1.4	5.5	12.0	30.0	5500
RG-16/U	52.0	0.630 in.	0.670	0.1	0.4	1.2	6.7	16.0	29.5	6000
RG-17A/U	50.0	0.870 in.	0.659	0.066	0.225	0.80	3.4	8.5	30.0	11000
RG-18A/U	50.0	0.945	0.659	0.066	0.225	0.80	3.4	8.5	30.5	11000
RG-19A/U	50.0	1.120 in.	0.659	0.04	0.17	0.68	3.5	7.7	30.5	14000
RG-20A/U	50.0	1.195 in.	0.659	0.04	0.17	0.68	3.5	7.7	30.5	14000
RG-21/AU	50.0	0.332 in.	0.659	1.4	4.4	13.0	43.0	85.0	30.0	2700
RG-29/U	53.5	0.184 in.	0.659	0.33	1.2	4.4	16.0	30.0	28.5	1900

Cable No.	Nominal Impedance Z_0 (ohms)	Cable Outside Diameter	Velocity Factor	Approximate Attenuation (dB per 100 ft.)					Capacity pF/ft.	Maximum Operating Voltage RMS
				1 MHz	10 MhZ	100 MHz	1000 MHz	3000 MHz		
RG-34A/U	75.0	0.630 in.	0.659	0.065	0.29	1.3	6.0	12.5	20.5	5200
RG-34B/U	75	0.630 in.	0.66		0.3	1.4	5.8		21.5	6500
RG-35A/U	75.0	0.945 in.	0.659	0.07	0.235	0.85	3.5	8.60	20.5	10000
RG-54A/U	58.0	0.250	0.659	0.18	0.74	3.1	11.5	21.5	26.5	3000
RG-55/U	53.5	0.206 in.	0.659	0.36	1.3	4.8	17.0	32.0	28.5	1900
RG-55A/U	50.0	0.216 in.	0.659	0.36	1.3	4.8	17.0	32.0	29.5	1900
RG-58/U	53.5	0.195 in.	0.659	0.33	1.25	4.65	17.5	37.5	28.5	1900
RG-58C/U	50.0	0.195 in.	0.659	0.42	1.4	4.9	24.0	45.0	30.0	1900
RG-59A/U	75.0	0.242 in.	0.659	0.34	1.10	3.40	12.0	26.0	20.5	2300
RG-59B/U	75	0.242	0.66		1.1	3.4	12		21	2300
RG-62A/U	93.0	0.242 in.	0.84	0.25	0.85	2.70	8.6	18.5	13.5	750
RG-74A/U	50.0	0.615 in.	0.659	0.10	0.38	1.5	6.0	11.5	30.0	5500
RG-83/U	35.0	0.405 in.	0.66	0.23	0.80	2.8	9.6	24.0	44.0	2000
*RG-213/U	50	0.405	0.66	0.16	0.6	1.9	8.0		29.5	5000
†RG-218/U	50	0.870	0.66	0.066	0.2	1.0	4.4		29.5	11000
‡RG-220/U	50	1.120	0.66	0.04	0.2	0.7	3.6		29.5	14000

* Formerly RG8A/U   † Formerly RG17A/U   ‡ Formerly RG19A/U

B.A. SCREWS

Size	Diameter		Threads per inch	Pitch		Hole size Clearance		Tapping	
	inches	mm		inches	mm	Size	No	Size	No
0	0.2362	6.0	25.4	0.0394	1.0	0.242	C	0.196	9
1	0.2087	5.3	28.2	0.0354	0.9	0.213	3	0.173	17
2	0.185	4.7	31.4	0.0319	0.81	0.1935	10	0.152	24
3	0.1614	4.1	34.8	0.0287	0.73	0.1695	18	0.128	30
4	0.1417	3.6	38.5	0.026	0.66	0.1495	25	0.116	32
5	0.126	3.2	43.0	0.0232	0.59	0.136	29	0.104	37
6	0.1102	2.8	47.9	0.0209	0.53	0.120	31	0.089	43
7	0.0984	2.5	52.9	0.0189	0.48	0.1065	36	0.081	46
8	0.0866	2.2	59.1	0.0169	0.43	0.0985	42	0.07	50
9	0.0748	1.9	65.1	0.0154	0.39	0.081	46	0.0595	53
10	0.0669	1.7	72.6	0.0138	0.35	0.073	49	0.055	54

METRIC THREADS

No.	Outside diameter (mm)	Pitch (mm)	Tapping (mm)	Clearance (mm)
M1	1.0	0.25	0.75	1.1
	1.6	0.35	1.25	1.7
M2	2.0	0.4	1.6	2.2
	2.5	0.45	2.05	2.7
	2.6	0.45	2.2	2.8
M3	3.0	0.5	2.5	3.2
M4	4.0	0.7	3.3	4.3
M5	5.0	0.8	4.2	5.3
M6	6.0	1.0	5.0	6.4
M8	8.0	1.25	6.7	8.4
M10	10.0	1.25	8.5	10.5
M12	12.0	1.75	10.3	13.0
M14	14.0	2.0	12.0	15.0
M16	16.0	2.0	14.0	17.0
M18	18.0	2.5	15.5	19.0
M20	20.0	2.5	17.5	21.0

TRANSMISSION LINES

1 PARALLEL STRIPS (SLAB LINES)

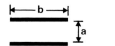

$$Z_0 \simeq 377 \frac{a}{b} \qquad \text{If } a \ll b$$
edge effects neglected

2 PARALLEL WIRE (TWIN LINE)

$$Z_0 = 276 \log_{10} \left(\frac{D}{d} + \sqrt{\left(\frac{D}{d}\right)^2 - 1} \right)$$

$$Z_0 \simeq 276 \log_{10} \frac{2D}{d} \qquad \text{if } d \ll D$$

3 WIRE PARALLEL TO INFINITE PLATE

$$Z_0 \simeq 138 \log_{10} \frac{D}{d} \qquad \text{if } d \ll D$$

4 WIRE PARALLEL TO TWO INFINITE PLATES

$$Z_0 \simeq 138 \log_{10} \frac{4D}{\pi d} \qquad \text{if } d \ll D$$

5 WIRE IN RECTANGULAR TROUGH

$$Z_0 \simeq 138 \log_{10} \left(\frac{4w \tan h \frac{\pi h}{w}}{\pi d} \right) \qquad \text{if } d \ll h, \text{ and } w$$

6 CIRCULAR COAXIAL

$$Z_0 = 138 \log_{10} \frac{D}{d}$$

7 SQUARE COAXIAL

$$Z_0 \simeq 138 \log_{10} \frac{1.178D}{d}$$

Note: In the above, the medium is taken as AIR.
For other medium, the resulting value of Z_0 should be multiplied by $\frac{1}{\sqrt{K}}$ where K is the dielectric constant

FUSE WIRE TABLE

Fusing Current	Copper Diameter	Copper S.W.G.	Tin Diameter	Tin S.W.G.	Lead Diameter	Lead S.W.G.
1 amp	0.0021	47	0.0072	37	0.0081	35
2 amp	0.0034	43	0.0113	31	0.0128	30
3 amp	0.0044	41	0.0149	28	0.0168	27
4 amp	0.0053	39	0.0181	26	0.0203	25
5 amp	0.0062	38	0.0210	25	0.0236	23
10 amp	0.0098	33	0.0334	21	0.0375	20
15 amp	0.0129	30	0.0437	19	0.0491	18
20 amp	0.0156	28	0.0529	17	0.0595	17

INTERNATIONAL PAPER SIZES

DESIGNATION	METRIC	IMPERIAL
A0	1189 × 841 mm	$46\frac{1}{4} \times 33\frac{1}{8}$ inches
A1	841 × 594 mm	$33\frac{1}{8} \times 23\frac{3}{8}$ inches
A2	594 × 420 mm	$23\frac{3}{8} \times 16\frac{1}{2}$ inches
A3	420 × 297 mm	$16\frac{1}{2} \times 11\frac{1}{4}$ inches
A4	297 × 210 mm	$11\frac{3}{4} \times 8\frac{1}{4}$ inches
A5	210 × 148 mm	$8\frac{1}{4} \times 5\frac{7}{8}$ inches
A6	148 × 105 mm	$5\frac{7}{8} \times 4\frac{1}{8}$ inches
A7	105 × 74 mm	$4\frac{1}{8} \times 2\frac{7}{8}$ inches

8 Measurements

THE INTERNATIONAL SYSTEM OF UNITS

The International System (SI) comprises six basic units which are listed below, together with the symbols assigned to them. Special names have been adopted for some of the derived SI units. The definitions of these units show the relationship between them and the basic units.

BASIC SI UNITS

Quantity	Name of unit	Unit symbol
electric current	ampere	A
length	metre	m
luminous intensity	candela	cd
mass	kilogram	kg
thermodynamic temperature	Kelvin	K
time	second	s

SI UNITS WITH SPECIAL NAMES

Physical quantity	SI unit	Unit symbol	
electric capacitance	farad	F	$= A\,s/V$
electric charge	coulomb	C	$= A\,s$
electrical potential	volt	V	$= W/A$
electric resistance	ohm	Ω	$= V/A$
force	newton	N	$= kg\,m/s^2$
frequency	hertz*	Hz	$= s^{-1}$
illumination	lux	lx	$= lm/m^2$
inductance	henry	H	$= V\,s/A$
luminous flux	lumen	lm	$= cd\,sr$
magnetic flux	weber	Wb	$= Vs$
magnetic flux density	tesla †	T	$= Wb/m^2$
power	watt	W	$= J/s$
work, energy, quantity of heat	joule	J	$= N\,m$

* Hertz is equivalent to cycle per second. † Tesla is equivalent to weber per square metre.

DERIVED SI UNITS WITH COMPLEX NAMES

Physical quantity	SI unit	Unit symbol
acceleration	metre per second squared	m/s^2
angular acceleration	radian per second squared	rad/s^2
angular velocity	radian per second	rad/s
area	square metre	m^2
density (mass density)	kilogram per cubic metre	kg/m^3
diffusion coefficient	metre squared per second	m^2/s
dynamic viscosity	newton second per metre squared	Ns/m^2
electric field strength	volt per metre	V/m
kinematic viscosity	metre squared per second	m^2/s
luminance	candela per square metre	cd/m^3
magnetic field strength	ampere per metre	A/m
pressure	newton per square metre	N/m^2
surface tension	newton per metre	N/m
thermal conductivity	watt per metre degree Kelvin	$W/(m\,^\circ K)$
velocity	metre per second	m/s
volume	cubic metre	m^3

REPRESENTATIONS OF UNITS (ISO 2955)

Name of unit	International symbol (common use symbol)	Representation Form I (double case)	Representation Form II (single case lower)	Representation Form II (single case upper)
Base SI units				
metre	m	m	m	M
kilogram	kg	kg	kg	KG
second	s	s	s	S
ampere	A	A	a	A
kelvin	K	K	k	K
mole	mol	mol	mol	MOL
candela	cd	cd	cd	CD
Supplementary SI units				
radian	rad	rad	rad	RAD
steradian	sr	sr	sr	SR

Name of unit	International symbol (common use) symbol)	Representation		
		Form I (double case)	Form II (single case lower)	(single case upper)
Derived SI units with special names				
hertz	Hz	HZ	hz	HZ
newton	N	N	n	N
pascal	Pa	Pa	pa	PA
joule	J	J	j	J
watt	W	W	w	W
coulomb	C	C	c	C
volt	V	V	v	V
farad	F	F	f	F
ohm	Ω	Ohm	ohm	OHM
siemens	S	S	sie	SIE
weber	Wb	Wb	wb	WB
tesla	T	T	t	T
henry	H	H	h	H
lumen	lm	lm	lm	LM
lux	lx	lx	lx	LX
Other units from ISO 1 000				
grade (angle)	^{g}(s)	gon	gon	GON
degree (angle)	$^{\circ}$ (s)	deg	deg	DEG
minute (angle)	$'$ (s)	$'$ (s)	mnt	MNT
second (angle)	$''$ (s)	$''$ (s)	sec	SEC
litre	l	l	l	L
are	a	a	are	ARE
minute (time)	min	min	min	MIN
hour	h	h	hr	HR
day	d	d	d	D
year	a	a	ann	ANN
gram	g	g	g	G
tonne	t	t	tne	TNE
bar	bar	bar	bar	BAR
poise	P	P	p	P
strokes	St	St	st	ST
electronvolt	eV	eV	ev	EV
degree Celsius	$^{\circ}$C	Cel	cel	CEL
atomic mass unit	u	u	u	U

CONVERSION FACTORS

To convert	into	Multiply by	Conversely — Multiply by
Amps	Milliamps	10^3	10^{-3}
Amp hours	Coulombs	3600	2.778×10^{-4}
Amp turns per cm.	Amp turns per inch	2.54	0.3937
Atmospheres	Lb/sq. in	14.70	0.068
B.T.U.	Foot pounds	778.3	1.285×10^{-3}
B.T.U.	Joules	1054.8	9.480×10^{-3}
B.T.U. per hour	H.P. hours	3.929×10^{-4}	2545
Centigrade	Fahrenheit	$\left({}^\circ C \times \dfrac{9}{5} \right) + 32 = {}^\circ F$	$({}^\circ F - 32) \dfrac{5}{9} = {}^\circ C$
Centigrade	Kelvin	${}^\circ C + 273 = {}^\circ K$	${}^\circ K - 273 = {}^\circ C$
Cubic inches	Cubic feet	5.787×10^{-4}	1728
Cubic inches	Cubic metres	1.639×10^{-5}	6.102×10^4
Degrees (angular)	Radians	1.745×10^{-2}	57.3
Dynes	Pounds	2.248×10^{-6}	4.448×10^5
Ergs	Foot pounds	7.376×10^{-8}	1.356×10^7
Farads	Microfarads	10^6	10^{-6}
Feet	Centimetres	30.48	3.281×10^{-2}
Foot-pounds	H.P. hours	5.05×10^{-7}	1.98×10^6
Foot pounds	Kilowatt hours	3.766×10^{-7}	2.655×10^6
Gausses	Lines per sq. in	6.452	0.155
Grams	Dynes	980.7	1.02×10^{-3}
Grams per cm.	Pounds per in	5.6×10^{-3}	178.6
Henrys	Microhenrys	10^6	10^{-6}
Horse power	B.T.U. per min	42.418	2.357×10^{-2}
Horse power	Foot lb per min	3.3×10^4	3.03×10^{-5}
Horse power	Foot lb per sec	550	1.818×10^{-3}
Horse power	Kilowatts	0.746	1.341
Inches	Centimetres	2.54	0.3937
Inches	Mils	10^3	10^{-3}
Kilograms	Pounds (lb)	2.205	0.454
Kilometres	Feet	3281	3.048×10^{-4}
Kilometres	Miles	0.621	1.609
Kilowatt hours	B.T.U.	3413	2.93×10^{-4}
Kilowatt hours	Joules	3.6×10^6	2.778×10^{-7}
Kilowatt hours	H.P. hours	1.341	0.7457
Knots	Miles per hour	1.1508	0.869
Lamberts	Candles per sq. cm	0.3183	3.142
Lamberts	Candles per sq. in	2.054	0.4869
Lumens per sq. ft	Foot candles	1	1
Lux	Foot candles	0.0929	10.764
Metres	Feet	3.28	0.3048
Metres	Yards	1.094	0.9144
Miles per hour	Feet per sec	1.467	0.68182
Nepers	Decibels	8.686	0.1151
Pounds of water	Cubic feet	1.603×10^{-2}	62.38
Pounds of water	Gallons	0.1	10
Tons	Pounds	2240	4.464×10^{-4}
Watts	Ergs per sec	10^7	10^{-7}

DECIBEL TABLE

Voltage ratio (equal impedance)	Power ratio	dB	Voltage ratio (equal impedance)	Power ratio
		← — + →		
1.000	1.000	0	1.000	1.000
0.989	0.977	0.1	1.012	1.023
0.977	0.955	0.2	1.023	1.047
0.966	0.933	0.3	1.035	1.072
0.955	0.912	0.4	1.047	1.096
0.944	0.891	0.5	1.059	1.122
0.933	0.871	0.6	1.072	1.148
0.923	0.851	0.7	1.084	1.175
0.912	0.832	0.8	1.096	1.202
0.902	0.813	0.9	1.109	1.230
0.891	0.794	1.0	1.122	1.259
0.841	0.708	1.5	1.189	1.413
0.794	0.631	2.0	1.259	1.585
0.750	0.562	2.5	1.334	1.778
0.708	0.501	3.0	1.413	1.995
0.668	0.447	3.5	1.496	2.239
0.631	0.398	4.0	1.585	2.512
0.596	0.355	4.5	1.679	2.818
0.562	0.316	5.0	1.779	3.162
0.531	0.282	5.5	1.884	3.548
0.501	0.251	6.0	1.995	3.981
0.473	0.224	6.5	2.113	4.467
0.447	0.200	7.0	2.239	5.012
0.422	0.178	7.5	2.371	5.623
0.398	0.159	8.0	2.512	6.310
0.376	0.141	8.5	2.661	7.079
0.355	0.126	9.0	2.818	7.943
0.335	0.112	9.5	2.985	8.913
0.316	0.100	10	3.162	10.00
0.282	0.0794	11	3.55	12.6
0.251	0.0631	12	3.98	15.9
0.224	0.0501	13	4.47	20.0
0.200	0.0398	14	5.01	25.1
0.178	0.0316	15	5.62	31.6
0.159	0.0251	16	6.31	39.8
0.141	0.0200	17	7.08	50.1
0.126	0.0159	18	7.94	63.1
0.112	0.0126	19	8.91	79.4
0.100	0.0100	20	10.00	100.0
3.16×10^{-2}	10^{-3}	30	3.16×10	10^2
10^{-2}	10^{-4}	40	10^2	10^4

Voltage ratio (equal impedance)	Power ratio		dB		Voltage ratio (equal impedance)	Power ratio
		←	−			
			+	→		
3.16×10^{-3}	10^{-5}		50		3.16×10^{2}	10^{5}
10^{-3}	10^{-6}		60		10^{3}	10^{6}
3.16×10^{-4}	10^{-7}		70		3.16×10^{3}	10^{7}
10^{-4}	10^{-8}		80		10^{4}	10^{8}
3.16×10^{-5}	10^{-9}		90		3.16×10^{4}	10^{9}
10^{-5}	10^{-10}		100		10^{5}	10^{10}
3.16×10^{-6}	10^{-11}		110		3.16×10^{5}	10^{11}
10^{-6}	10^{-12}		120		10^{6}	10^{12}

FREQUENCY v WAVELENGTH FOR RADIO WAVES

The velocity of propagation of a wave is:

$$v = f\lambda \text{ centimetres per second}$$

(where f = frequency in hertz (cycles per second) and λ = wavelength in centimetres).

For electromagnetic waves in free space the velocity of propagation, v, is approximately 3×10^{10} cm per second. If f (frequency) is expressed in kilohertz (kHz) and λ (wavelength) in metres, the following can be used:

$$f = \frac{300,000}{\lambda} \text{ kHz} \qquad \text{or} \qquad \lambda = \frac{300,000}{f} \text{ metres}$$

For a frequency expressed in meghertz (MHz):

$$f = \frac{300}{\lambda} \text{ MHz} \qquad \text{or} \qquad \lambda = \frac{300}{f} \text{ metres}$$

Datum Points:

f, MHz	λ, metres
1	300
3	100
10	30
30	10
100	3
300	1
1000	0.3

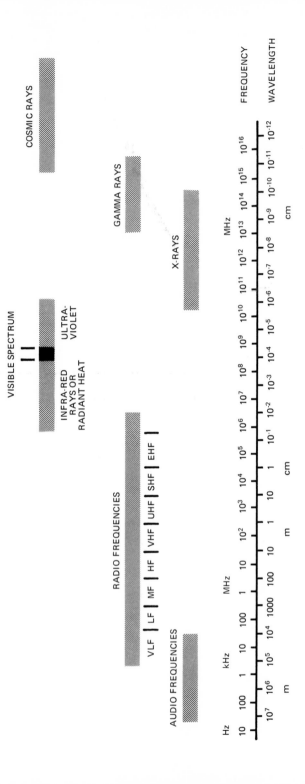

THE ELECTROMAGNETIC WAVE SPECTRUM

MULTIPLIERS

The names of multiples and sub-multiples of units are formed by means of the prefixes shown in this table.

Factor by which the unit is multiplied	Prefix	Symbol
$1\ 000\ 000\ 000\ 000 = 10^{12}$	tera	T
$1\ 000\ 000\ 000 = 10^{9}$	giga	G
$1\ 000\ 000 = 10^{6}$	mega	M
$1\ 000 = 10^{3}$	kilo	k
$100 = 10^{2}$	hecto	h
$10 = 10^{1}$	deca	da
$0.1 = 10^{-1}$	deci	d
$0.01 = 10^{-2}$	centi	c
$0.001 = 10^{-3}$	milli	m
$0.000\ 001 = 10^{-6}$	micro	μ
$0.000\ 000\ 001 = 10^{-9}$	nano	n
$0.000\ 000\ 000\ 001 = 10^{-12}$	pico	p
$0.000\ 000\ 000\ 000\ 001 = 10^{-15}$	femto	f
$0.000\ 000\ 000\ 000\ 000\ 001 = 10^{-18}$	atto	a

REPRESENTATIONS OF PREFIXES

Prefix	Factor by which the unit is multiplied	International symbol (common use symbol)	Representation		
			Form I (double case)	Form II (single case lower)	Form II (single case upper)
tera	10^{12}	T	T	t	T
giga	10^{9}	G	G	g	G
mega	10^{6}	M	M	ma	MA
kilo	10^{3}	k	k	k	K
hecto	10^{2}	h	h	h	H
deca	10^{1}	da	da	da	DA
deci	10^{-1}	d	d	d	D
centi	10^{-2}	c	c	c	C
milli	10^{-3}	m	m	m	M
micro	10^{-6}	μ	u	u	U
nano	10^{-9}	n	n	n	N
pico	10^{-12}	p	p	p	P
femto	10^{-15}	f	f	f	F
atto	10^{-18}	a	a	a	A

9 Radio

SIGNAL REPORTING CODES

1 SINPO (ITU Radio Regulations)

Scale Rating	Signal Strength	Interference	Noise	Propagation Disturbance	Overall Rating
	S	I	N	P	O
5	Excellent	Nil	Nil	Nil	Excellent
4	Good	Slight	Slight	Slight	Good
3	Fair	Moderate	Moderate	Moderate	Fair
2	Poor	Severe	Severe	Severe	Poor
1	Barely audible	Extreme	Extreme	Extreme	Unusable

2 RST (Conventional)

Scale Rating	Readability	Strength	Tone (CW only)
	R	S	T
1	Unreadable	Barely perceptible	60 Hz or less, very rough and broad
2	Barely readable	Very weak	Very rough a c, harsh and broad
3	Readable with considerable difficulty	Weak	Rough a c, rectified not filtered
4	Readable with practically no difficulty	Fair	Rough note
5	Perfectly readable	Fairly good	Filtered, but ripple modulated
6	–	Good	Filtered tone, trace of ripple
7	–	Moderately strong	Near pure tone, trace of ripple
8	–	Strong	Near perfect tone, trace of modulation
9	–	Extremely strong	Perfect tone

˙An X can be added to indicate the characteristic steadiness of crystal control
A C can be added to indicate chirp
A K can be added to indicate key clicks

3 SINPFEMO (ITU Radio Regulations)

Rating Scale	Signal Strength S	Interference I	Degrading Effect of Modulation			Quality E	Depth M	Overall Rating O
			Noise N	Propagation Disturbance P	Frequency of Fading F			
5	Excellent	Nil	Nil	Nil	Nil	Excellent	Maximum	Excellent
4	Good	Slight	Slight	Slight	Slow	Good	Good	Good
3	Fair	Moderate	Moderate	Moderate	Moderate	Fair	Fair	Fair
2	Poor	Severe	Severe	Severe	Fast	Poor	Poor or nil	Poor
1	Barely audible	Extreme	Extreme	Extreme	Very fast	Very poor	Continuously overmodulated	Unusable

NOMENCLATURE FOR FREQUENCY AND WAVELENGTH BANDS

(ITU Radio Regulations)

The unit of frequency is expressed:
- in kilohertz (kHz) up to and including 3000 kHz
- in megahertz (MHz), from 3 MHz up to and including 3000 MHz
- in gigahertz (GHz), from 3 GHz up to and including 3000 GHz
- in terahertz (THz), above 300 GHz

FREQUENCY BANDS

Band number	Symbol	Frequency range	Corresponding metric subdivision
4	VLF	3–30 kHz	Myriametric waves
5	LF	30–300 kHz	Kilometric waves
6	MF	300–3000 kHz	Hectometric waves
7	HF	3–30 MHz	Decametric waves
8	VHF	30–300 MHz	Metric waves
9	UHF	300–3000 MHz	Decimetric waves
10	SHF	3–30 GHz	Centimetric waves
11	EHF	30–300 GHz	Millimetric waves
12		300–3000 GHz	Decimillimetric waves

Note: Band number n extends from 0.3×10^n Hz to 3×10^n Hz.

INTERNATIONAL FREQUENCY ALLOCATIONS (0–150 MHz)

(Proceedings of World Administrative Radio Conference, 1979, ITU Radio Regulations, 1982)

Notes
There are a great many footnotes which modify the allocations in different countries or different regions (particularly above 30 MHz).

Entries in capital letters are primary or permitted services, others are secondary services. The latter must not cause interference to primary services and cannot claim protection from interference caused by primary services.

Services are listed alphabetically according to the original French language and do not indicate relative priority.

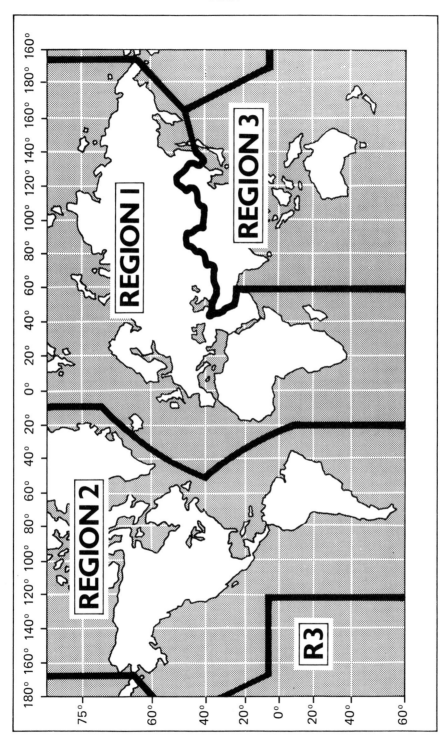

Region 1	Region 2	Region 3
Below 9 kHz	not allocated	
9 – 14 kHz	RADIO NAVIGATION	
14 – 19.95 kHz	FIXED MARITIME MOBILE	
19.95 – 20.05 kHz	STANDARD FREQUENCY AND TIME SIGNAL (20 kHz)	
20.05 – 70 kHz	FIXED MARITIME MOBILE	
70 – 72 kHz RADIONAVIGATION	70 – 90 kHz FIXED MARITIME MOBILE Radiolocation	70 – 72 kHz RADIONAVIGATION FIXED Maritime Mobile
72 – 84 kHz FIXED MARITIME MOBILE RADIONAVIGATION		72 – 84 kHz FIXED MARITIME MOBILE RADIONAVIGATION
84 – 86 kHz RADIONAVIGATION		84 – 86 kHz RADIONAVIGATION FIXED Maritime Mobile
86 – 90 kHz FIXED MARITIME MOBILE RADIONAVIGATION		86 – 90 kHz FIXED MARITIME MOBILE RADIONAVIGATION
90 – 110 kHz	RADIONAVIGATION FIXED Maritime Mobile	
110 – 112 kHz FIXED MARITIME MOBILE RADIONAVIGATION	110 – 130 kHz FIXED MARITIME MOBILE MARITIME RADIO- NAVIGATION Radiolocation	110 – 112 kHz FIXED MARITIME MOBILE RADIONAVIGATION
112 – 115 kHz RADIONAVIGATION		112 – 117.6 kHz RADIONAVIGATION FIXED Maritime Mobile
115 – 117.6 kHz RADIONAVIGATION FIXED Maritime Mobile		

Region 1	Region 2	Region 3
117.6 – 126 kHz FIXED MARITIME MOBILE RADIONAVIGATION		117.6 – 126 kHz FIXED MARITIME MOBILE RADIONAVIGATION
126 – 129 kHz RADIONAVIGATION		126 – 129 kHz RADIONAVIGATION fixed Maritime Mobile
129 – 130 kHz FIXED MARITIME MOBILE RADIONAVIGATION		129 – 130 kHz FIXED MARITIME MOBILE RADIONAVIGATION
130 – 148.5 kHz MARITIME MOBILE FIXED	130 – 160 kHz FIXED MARITIME MOBILE	130 – 160 kHz FIXED MARITIME MOBILE RADIONAVIGATION
148.5 – 255 kHz BROADCASTING	160 – 190 kHz FIXED	160 – 190 kHz FIXED Aeronautical Radionavigation
255 – 283.5 kHz BROADCASTING AERONAUTICAL RADIONAVIGATION	190 – 200 kHz AERONAUTICAL RADIONAVIGATION	
283.5 – 315 kHz MARITIME RADIONAVI- GATION AERONAUTICAL RADIONAVIGATION	200 – 285 kHz AERONAUTICAL RADIONAVIGATION Aeronautical Mobile	
	285 – 315 kHz MARITIME RADIONAVIGATION AERONAUTICAL RADIONAVIGATION	
315 – 325 kHz AERONAUTICAL RADIO- NAVIGATION Maritime Radionavigation	315 – 325 kHz MARITIME RADIO- NAVIGATION Aeronautical Radio- navigation	315 – 325 kHz AERONAUTICAL RADIO- NAVIGATION MARITIME RADIO- NAVIGATION
325 – 405 kHz AERONAUTICAL RADIO- NAVIGATION	325 – 335 kHz AERONAUTICAL RADIO- NAVIGATION Aeronautical Mobile Maritime Radionavigation	325 – 405 kHz AERONAUTICAL RADIO- NAVIGATION Aeronautical Mobile
	335 – 405 kHz AERONAUTICAL RADIO- NAVIGATION Aeronautical Mobile	

Region 1	Region 2	Region 3
405 – 415 kHz RADIONAVIGATION	405 – 415 kHz RADIONAVIGATION Aeronautical Mobile	
415 – 435 kHz AERONAUTICAL RADIO- NAVIGATION MARITIME MOBILE	415 – 495 kHz MARITIME MOBILE	
435 – 495 kHz MARITIME MOBILE Aeronautical Radionavigation		
495 – 505 kHz	MOBILE (distress and calling)	
505 – 526.5 kHz MARITIME MOBILE AERONAUTICAL RADIO- NAVIGATION	505 – 510 kHz MARITIME MOBILE	505 – 526.5 kHz MARITIME MOBILE AERONAUTICAL RADIO- NAVIGATION Aeronautical Mobile Land Mobile
526.5 – 1606.5 kHz BROADCASTING	510 – 525 kHz MOBILE AERONAUTICAL RADIO- NAVIGATION	
	525 – 535 kHz BROADCASTING AERONAUTICAL RADIO- NAVIGATION	526.5 – 535 kHz BROADCASTING Mobile
	535 –1606.5 kHz BROADCASTING	535 –1606.5 kHz BROADCASTING
1606.5 – 1625 kHz MARITIME MOBILE FIXED LAND MOBILE	1606.5 –1625 kHz BROADCASTING	1606.5 –1800 kHz FIXED MOBILE RADIOLOCATION RADIONAVIGATION
1625 – 1635 kHz RADIOLOCATION	1625 –1705 kHz BROADCASTING FIXED MOBILE	
1635 – 1800 kHz MARITIME MOBILE FIXED LAND MOBILE	1705 –1800 kHz FIXED MOBILE RADIOLOCATION AERONAUTICAL RADIO- NAVIGATION	

Region 1	Region 2	Region 3
1800 — 1810 kHz RADIOLOCATION	1800 —1850 kHz AMATEUR	1800 —2000 kHz AMATEUR FIXED MOBILE (except Aeronautical Mobile) RADIONAVIGATION Radiolocation
1810 — 1850 kHz AMATEUR		
1850 — 2000 kHz FIXED MOBILE (except Aeronautical Mobile)	1850 —2000 kHz AMATEUR FIXED MOBILE (except Aeronautical Mobile) RADIOLOCATION RADIONAVIGATION	
2000 — 2025 kHz FIXED MOBILE (except Aeronautical Mobile)	2000 —2065 kHz FIXED MOBILE	
2025 — 2045 kHz FIXED MOBILE (except Aeronautical Mobile) Meterological Aids	2065 —2107 kHz MARITIME MOBILE	
2045 — 2160 kHz MARITIME MOBILE FIXED LAND MOBILE	2107 —2170 kHz FIXED MOBILE	
2160 — 2170 kHz RADIOLOCATION		
2170 — 2173.5 kHz MARITIME MOBILE		
2173.5 — 2190.5 kHz MOBILE (Distress and Calling)		
2190.5 — 2194 kHz MARITIME MOBILE		
2194 — 2300 kHz FIXED MOBILE (except Aeronautical Mobile)	2194 —2300 kHz FIXED MOBILE	
2300 — 2498 kHz FIXED MOBILE (except Aeronautical Mobile) BROADCASTING	2300 —2495 kHz FIXED MOBILE BROADCASTING	

Region 1	Region 2	Region 3
2498 – 2501 kHz STANDARD FREQUENCY AND TIME SIGNAL	2495 –2501 kHz STANDARD FREQUENCY AND TIME SIGNAL	
2501 – 2502 kHz	STANDARD FREQUENCY AND TIME SIGNAL Space Research	
2502 – 2625 kHz FIXED MOBILE (except Aeronautical Mobile)	2505 –2850 kHz FIXED MOBILE	
2625 – 2650 kHz MARITIME MOBILE MARITIME RADIO-NAVIGATION		
2650 – 2850 kHz FIXED MOBILE (except Aeronautical Mobile)		
2850 – 3025 kHz	AERONAUTICAL MOBILE (R)	
3025 – 3155 kHz	AERONAUTICAL MOBILE (OR)	
3155 – 3200 kHz	FIXED MOBILE (except Aeronautical)	
3200 – 3400 kHz	FIXED MOBILE (except Aeronautical) BROADCASTING	
3400 – 3500 kHz	AERONAUTICAL MOBILE (R)	
3500 – 3800 kHz AMATEUR FIXED MOBILE (except Aeronautical)	3500 –3750 kHz AMATEUR 3750 –4000 kHz AMATEUR FIXED MOBILE (except Aeronautical)	3500 –3900 kHz AMATEUR FIXED MOBILE
3800 – 3900 kHz FIXED AERONAUTICAL MOBILE (OR) LAND MOBILE		
3900 – 3950 kHz AERONAUTICAL MOBILE		3900 –3950 kHz AERONAUTICAL MOBILE BROADCASTING
3950 – 4000 kHz FIXED BROADCASTING		3950 –4000 kHz FIXED BROADCASTING

Region 1	Region 2	Region 3
4000 – 4438 kHz FIXED MARITIME MOBILE		
4438 – 4650 kHz FIXED MOBILE (except Aeronautical)		
4650 – 4700 kHz AERONAUTICAL MOBILE (R)		
4700 – 4750 kHz AERONAUTICAL MOBILE (OR)		
4750 – 4850 kHz FIXED AERONAUTICAL MOBILE LAND MOBILE BROADCASTING	4750 –4850 kHz FIXED MOBILE (except Aeronautical) BROADCASTING	4750 –4850 kHz FIXED BROADCASTING Land Mobile
4850 – 4995 kHz FIXED LAND MOBILE BROADCASTING		
4995 – 5003 kHz STANDARD FREQUENCY AND TIME SIGNAL		
5003 – 5005 kHz STANDARD FREQUENCY AND TIME SIGNAL Space Research		
5005 – 5060 kHz FIXED BROADCASTING		
5060 – 5450 kHz FIXED Mobile (except Aeronautical)		
5450 – 5480 kHz FIXED AERONAUTICAL MOBILE (OR) LAND MOBILE	5450 –5480 kHz AERONAUTICAL MOBILE	5450 –5480 kHz FIXED AERONAUTICAL MOBILE (OR) LAND MOBILE
5480 – 5680 kHz AERONAUTICAL MOBILE (R)		
5680 – 5730 kHz AERONAUTICAL MOBILE (OR)		
5730 – 5950 kHz FIXED LAND MOBILE	5730 –5950 kHz FIXED MOBILE (except Aeronautical)	
5950 – 6200 kHz BROADCASTING		
6200 – 6525 kHz MARITIME MOBILE		
6525 – 6685 kHz AERONAUTICAL MOBILE (R)		
6685 – 6765 kHz AERONAUTICAL MOBILE (OR)		

Region 1	Region 2	Region 3
6765 — 7000 kHz	FIXED Land Mobile	
7000 — 7100 kHz	AMATEUR AMATEUR — SATELLITE	
7100 — 7300 kHz BROADCASTING	7100 —7300 kHz AMATEUR	7100 —7300 kHz BROADCASTING
7300 — 8100 kHz	FIXED Land Mobile	
8100 — 8195 kHz	FIXED MARITIME MOBILE	
8195 — 8815 kHz	MARITIME MOBILE	
8815 — 8965 kHz	AERONAUTICAL MOBILE (R)	
8965 — 9040 kHz	AERONAUTICAL MOBILE (OR)	
9040 — 9500 kHz	FIXED	
9500 — 9900 kHz	BROADCASTING	
9900 — 9995 kHz	FIXED	
9995 —10 003 kHz	STANDARD FREQUENCY AND TIME SIGNAL (10 000 kHz)	
10 003 —10 005 kHz	STANDARD FREQUENCY AND TIME SIGNAL Space Research	
10 005 —10 100 kHz	AERONAUTICAL MOBILE	
10 100 —10 150 kHz	FIXED Amateur	
10 150 —11 175 kHz	FIXED Mobile (except Aeronautical)	
11 175 —11 275 kHz	AERONAUTICAL MOBILE (OR)	
11 275 —11 400 kHz	AERONAUTICAL MOBILE (R)	
11 400 —11 650 kHz	FIXED	
11 650 —12 050 kHz	BROADCASTING	
12 050 —12 230 kHz	FIXED	
12 230 —13 200 kHz	MARITIME MOBILE	

	Region 1		Region 2	Region 3
13 200	−13 260	kHz	AERONAUTICAL MOBILE (OR)	
13 260	−13 360	kHz	AERONAUTICAL MOBILE (R)	
13 360	−13 410	kHz	FIXED RADIO ASTRONOMY	
13 410	−13 600	kHz	FIXED Mobile (except Aeronautical)	
13 600	−13 800	kHz	BROADCASTING	
13 800	−14 000	kHz	FIXED Mobile (except Aeronautical)	
14 000	−14 250	kHz	AMATEUR AMATEUR − SATELLITE	
14 250	−14 350	kHz	AMATEUR	
14 350	−14 990	kHz	FIXED Mobile (except Aeronautical)	
14 990	−15 005	kHz	STANDARD FREQUENCY AND TIME SIGNAL (15 000 kHz)	
15 005	−15 010	kHz	STANDARD FREQUENCY AND TIME SIGNAL Space Research	
15 010	−15 100	kHz	AERONAUTICAL MOBILE (OR)	
15 100	−15 600	kHz	BROADCASTING	
15 600	−16 360	kHz	FIXED	
16 360	−17 410	kHz	MARITIME MOBILE	
17 410	−17 550	kHz	FIXED	
17 550	−17 900	kHz	BROADCASTING	
17 900	−17 970	kHz	AERONAUTICAL MOBILE (R)	
17 970	−18 030	kHz	AERONAUTICAL MOBILE (OR)	
18 030	−18 052	kHz	FIXED	
18 052	−18 068	kHz	FIXED Space Research	
18 068	−18 168	kHz	AMATEUR AMATEUR − SATELLITE	

	Region 1		Region 2	Region 3
18 168	−18 780	kHz	FIXED	
18 780	−18 900	kHz	MARITIME MOBILE	
18 900	−19 680	kHz	FIXED	
19 680	−19 800	kHz	MARITIME MOBILE	
19 800	−19 990	kHz	FIXED	
19 990	−19 995	kHz	STANDARD FREQUENCY AND TIME SIGNAL Space Research	
19 995	−20 010	kHz	STANDARD FREQUENCY AND TIME SIGNAL (20 000 kHz)	
20 010	−21 000	kHz	FIXED MOBILE	
21 000	−21 450	kHz	AMATEUR AMATEUR − SATELLITE	
21 450	−21 850	kHz	BROADCASTING	
21 850	−21 870	kHz	FIXED	
21 870	−21 924	kHz	AERONAUTICAL FIXED	
21 924	−22 000	kHz	AERONAUTICAL MOBILE (R)	
22 000	−22 855	kHz	MARITIME MOBILE	
22 855	−23 000	kHz	FIXED	
23 000	−23 200	kHz	FIXED MOBILE (except Aeronautical)	
23 200	−23 350	kHz	AERONAUTICAL FIXED AERONAUTICAL MOBILE (OR)	
23 350	−24 000	kHz	FIXED MOBILE (except Aeronautical)	
24 000	−24 890	kHz	FIXED LAND MOBILE	
24 890	−24 990	kHz	AMATEUR AMATEUR − SATELLITE	
24 990	−25 005	kHz	STANDARD FREQUENCY AND TIME SIGNAL (25 000 kHz)	

	Region 1		Region 2	Region 3
25 005	−25 010	kHz	STANDARD FREQUENCY AND TIME SIGNAL Space Research	
25 010	−25 070	kHz	FIXED MOBILE (except Aeronautical)	
25 070	−25 210	kHz	MARITIME MOBILE	
25 210	−25 550	kHz	FIXED MOBILE (except Aeronautical)	
25 550	−25 670	kHz	RADIO ASTRONOMY	
25 670	−26 100	kHz	BROADCASTING	
26 100	−26 175	kHz	MARITIME MOBILE	
26 175	−27 500	kHz	FIXED MOBILE (except Aeronautical)	
27.5 −	28	MHz	METEOROLOGICAL AIDS FIXED MOBILE	
28 −	29.7	MHz	AMATEUR AMATEUR − SATELLITE	
29.7 −	30.005	MHz	FIXED MOBILE	
30.005−	30.01	MHz	SPACE OPERATION (Satellite Identification) FIXED MOBILE SPACE RESEARCH	
30.01 −	37.5	MHz	FIXED MOBILE	
37.5 −	38.25	MHz	FIXED MOBILE Radio Astronomy	
38.25 −	39.986	MHz	FIXED MOBILE	
39.986−	40.02	MHz	FIXED MOBILE Space Research	
40.02 −	40.98	MHz	FIXED MOBILE	

Region 1	Region 2	Region 3
40.98 – 41.015 MHz FIXED MOBILE Space Research		
41.015– 47 MHz FIXED MOBILE		
47 – 68 MHz BROADCASTING	47 – 50 MHz FIXED MOBILE	47 – 50 MHz FIXED MOBILE BROADCASTING
	50 – 54 MHz AMATEUR	
	54 – 68 MHz BROADCASTING	54 – 68 MHz FIXED MOBILE BROADCASTING
68 – 74.8 MHz FIXED MOBILE (except Aero- nautical)	68 – 72 MHz BROADCASTING Fixed Mobile	68 – 74.8 MHz FIXED MOBILE
	72 – 73 MHz FIXED MOBILE	
	73 – 74.6 MHz RADIO ASTRONOMY	
	74.6 – 74.8 MHz FIXED MOBILE	
74.8 – 75.2 MHz AERONAUTICAL RADIONAVIGATION		
75.2 – 87.5 MHz FIXED MOBILE (except Aero- nautical)	75.2 – 76 MHz FIXED MOBILE	75.2 – 87 MHz FIXED MOBILE
	76 – 88 MHz BROADCASTINING Fixed Mobile	
87.5 – 100 MHz BROADCASTING	88 – 100 MHz BROADCASTING	87 – 100 MHz FIXED MOBILE BROADCASTING
100 – 108 MHz BROADCASTING		

Region 1	Region 2	Region 3
108 – 117.975 MHz AERONAUTICAL RADIONAVIGATION		
117.975– 136 MHz AERONAUTICAL MOBILE Fixed Mobile (except Aeronautical)		
137 – 138 MHz SPACE OPERATION METEOROLOGICAL SATELLITE SPACE RESEARCH Fixed Mobile (except Aeronautical)		
138 – 143.6 MHz AERONAUTICAL MOBILE (OR)	138 – 143.6 MHz FIXED MOBILE RADIOLOCATION Space Research	138 – 143.6 MHz FIXED MOBILE Space Research
143.6 – 143.65 MHz AERONAUTICAL MOBILE SPACE RESEARCH	143.6 – 143.65 MHz FIXED MOBILE SPACE RESEARCH RADIOLOCATION	143.6 – 143.65 MHz FIXED MOBILE SPACE RESEARCH
143.65 – 144 MHz AERONAUTICAL MOBILE (OR)	143.65– 144 MHz FIXED MOBILE RADIOLOCATION Space Research	143.65– 144 MHz FIXED MOBILE Space Research
144 – 146 MHz AMATEUR AMATEUR – SATELLITE		
146 – 149.9 MHz FIXED MOBILE (except Aero- nautical)	146 – 148 MHz AMATEUR	146 – 148 MHz AMATEUR FIXED MOBILE
	148 – 149.9 MHz FIXED MOBILE	
149.9 – 150 MHz RADIONAVIGATION-SATELLITE		

THE IONOSPHERE

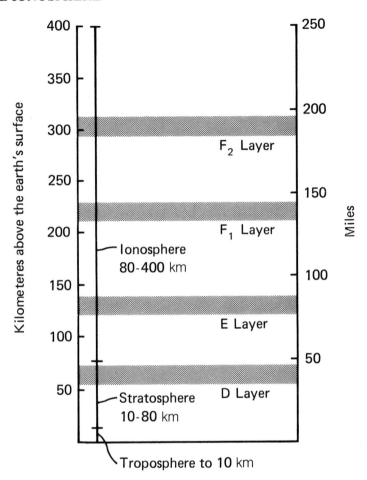

ALLOCATION OF INTERNATIONAL CALL SIGN SERIES (AS DEFINED BY ITU)

AA–AL	U.S.A.	A9	Bahrain
AM–AO	Spain	B	China
AP–AS	Pakistan	CA–CE	Chile
AT–AW	India	CF–CK	Canada
AX	Australia	CL–CM	Cuba
AY–AZ	Argentina	CN	Morocco
A2	Botswana	CO	Cuba
A3	Tonga	CP	Bolivia
A4	Oman	CQ–CU	Portugal
A5	Bhutan	CV–CX	Uruguay
A6	United Arab Emirates	CY–CZ	Canada
A7	Qatar	C2	Nauru
A8	Liberia	C3	Andorra

C4	Cyprus	JW–JX	Norway
C5	Gambia	JY	Jordan
C6	Bahamas	JZ	Indonesia
C7	World Meteorological Organization	J2	Djibouti
C8–C9	Mozambique	J3	Grenada
DA–DR	Germany (Federal Republic of)	J4	Greece
DS–DT	Korea (Republic of)	J5	Guinea-Bissau
DU–DZ	Philippines	J6	Saint Lucia
D2–D3	Angola	J7	Dominica
D4	Cape Verde	J8	Saint Vincent and the Grenadines
D5	Liberia	K	U.S.A.
D6	Comoro Islands	LA–LN	Norway
D7–D9	Korea (Republic of)	LO–LW	Argentina
EA–EH	Spain	LX	Luxembourg
EI–EJ	Ireland	LY	U.S.S.R.
EK	U.S.S.R.	LZ	Bulgaria
EL	Liberia	L2–L9	Argentina
EM–EO	U.S.S.R.	M	United Kingdom
EP–EQ	Iran	N	U.S.A.
ER–ES	U.S.S.R.	OA–OC	Peru
ET	Ethiopia	OD	Lebanon
EU–EW	Byelorussia	OE	Austria
EX–EZ	U.S.S.R.	OF–OJ	Finland
F	France	OK–OM	Czechoslovakia
G	United Kingdom	ON–OT	Belgium
HA	Hungary	OU–OZ	Denmark
HB	Switzerland	PA–PI	Netherlands
HC–HD	Ecuador	PJ	Netherlands Antilles
HE	Switzerland	PK–PO	Indonesia
HF	Poland	PP–PY	Brazil
HG	Hungary	PZ	Surinam
HH	Haiti	P2	Papua New Guinea
HI	Dominican Republic	P3	Cyprus
HJ–HK	Colombia	P4	Netherlands Antilles
HL	Korea (Republic of)	P5–P9	Korea (Democratic People's Republic of
HM	Korea (Democratic People's Republic of)	Q	(Service abbreviations)
HN	Iraq	R	U.S.S.R.
HO–HP	Panama (Republic of)	SA–SM	Sweden
HQ–HR	Honduras	SN–SR	Poland
HS	Thailand	SSA--SSM	Egypt
HT	Nicaragua	SSN–STZ	Sudan
HU	El Salvador	SU	Egypt
HV	Vatican City State	SV–SZ	Greece
HW–HY	France	S2–S3	Bangladesh
HZ	Saudi Arabia	S6	Singapore
H2	Cyprus	S7	Seychelles
H3	Panama (Republic of)	S9	São Tomé and Principe
H4	Solomon Islands	TA–TC	Turkey
H5	Bophuthatswana	TD	Guatemala
H6–H7	Nicaragua	TE	Costa Rica
H8–H9	Panama	TF	Iceland
I	Italy	TG	Guatemala
JA–JS	Japan	TH	France
JT–JV	Mongolia	TI	Costa Rica

TJ	Cameroon	ZA	Albania
TK	France	ZB–ZJ	United Kingdom
TL	Central African Republic	ZK–ZM	New Zealand
TM	France	ZN–ZO	United Kingdom
TN	Congo	ZP	Paraguay
TO–TQ	France	ZQ	United Kingdom
TR	Gabon	ZR–ZU	South Africa (Republic of)
TS	Tunisia	ZV–ZZ	Brazil
TT	Chad	Z2	Zimbabwe
TU	Ivory Coast	2	United Kingdom
TV–TX	France	3A	Monaco
TY	Benin	3B	Mauritius
TZ	Mali	3C	Equatorial Guinea
T2	Tuvalu	3DA–3DM	Swaziland
T3	Kiribati	3DN–3DZ	Fiji
T4	Cuba	3E–3F	Panama (Republic of)
T5	Somalia	3G	Chile
T6	Afghanistan	3H–3U	China
UA–UQ	U.S.S.R.	3V	Tunisia
UR–UT	Ukrainia	3W	Vietnam
UU–UZ	U.S.S.R.	3X	Guinea
VA–VG	Canada	3Y	Norway
VH–VN	Australia	3Z	Poland
VO	Canada	4A–4C	Mexico
VP–VS	United Kingdom	4D–4I	Philippines
VT–VW	India	4J–4L	U.S.S.R.
VX–VY	Canada	4M	Venezuela
VZ	Australia	4N–4O	Yugoslavia
V2	Antigua	4P–4S	Sri Lanka
W	U.S.A.	4T	Peru
XA–XI	Mexico	4U	United Nations Organisation
XJ–XO	Canada	4V	Haiti
XP	Denmark	4W	Yemen Arab Republic
XQ–XR	Chile	4X	Israel
XS	China	4Y	International Civil Aviation Organisation
XT	Upper Volta		
XU	Kampuchea	4Z	Israel
XV	Vietnam	5A	Libya
XW	Laos	5B	Cyprus
XX	Portugal	5C–5G	Morocco
XY–XZ	Burma	5H–5I	Tanzania
YA	Afghanistan	5J–5K	Colombia
YB–YH	Indonesia	5L–5M	Liberia
YI	Iraq	5N–5O	Nigeria
YJ	Vanuatu	5P–5Q	Denmark
YK	Syria	5R–5S	Madagascar
YL	U.S.S.R.	5T	Mauritania
YM	Turkey	5U	Niger
YN	Nicaragua	5V	Togo
YO–YR	Romania	5W	Western Samoa
YS	El Salvador	5X	Uganda
YT–YU	Yugoslavia	5Y–5Z	Kenya
YV–YY	Venezuela	6A–6B	Egypt
YZ	Yugoslavia	6C	Syria
Y2–Y9	German Democratic Republic	6D–6J	Mexico

6K-6N	Korea (Republic of)	8Q	Maldives
6O	Somalia	8R	Guyana
6P-6S	Pakistan	8S	Sweden
6T-6U	Sudan	8T-8Y	India
6V-6W	Senegal	8Z	Saudi Arabia
6X	Madagascar	9A	San Marino
6Y	Jamaica	9B-9D	Iran
6Z	Liberia	9E-9F	Ethiopia
7A-7I	Indonesia	9G	Ghana
7J-7N	Japan	9H	Malta
7O	Yemen (People's Democratic Republic of)	9I-9J	Zambia
		9K	Kuwait
7P	Lesotho	9L	Sierra Leone
7Q	Malawi	9M	Malaysia
7R	Algeria	9N	Nepal
7S	Sweden	9O-9T	Zaire
7T-7Y	Algeria	9U	Burundi
7Z	Saudi Arabia	9V	Singapore
8A-8I	Indonesia	9W	Malaysia
8J-8N	Japan	9X	Rwanda
8O	Botswana	9Y-9Z	Trinidad and Tobago
8P	Barbados		

WORLD TELEVISION SYSTEMS

System	Lines	Channel Band-width	Vision Band-width	Sound Vision Separation	Vestigial Sideband	Modulaltion Vision	Modulaltion Sound
A	405	5 MHz	3 MHz	−3.5 MHz	0.75 MHz	Postive	A.M.
B	625	7 MHz	5 MHz	+5.5 MHz	0.75 MHz	Negative	F.M.
C	625	7 MHz	5 MHz	+5.5 MHz	0.75 MHz	Positive	A.M.
D	625	8 MHz	6 MHz	+6.5 MHz	0.75 MHz	Negative	F.M.
E	819	14 MHz	10 MHz	±11.15 MHz	2 MHz	Positive	A.M.
F	819	7 MHz	5 MHz	+5.5 MHz	0.75 MHz	Positive	A.M.
G	625	8 MHz	5 MHz	+5.5 MHz	0.75 MHz	Negative	F.M.
H	625	8 MHz	5 MHz	+5.5 MHz	1.25 MHz	Negative	F.M.
I	625	8 MHz	5.5 MHz	+6 MHz	1.25 MHz	Negative	F.M.
K	625	8 MHz	6 MHz	+6.5 MHz	0.75 MHz	Negative	F.M.
K'	625	4 MHz	6 MHz	+6.5 MHz	1.25 MHz	Negative	F.M.
L	625	8 MHz	6 MHz	+6.5 MHz	1.25 MHz	Positive	A.M.
M	525	6 MHz	4.2 MHz	+4.5 MHz	0.75 MHz	Negative	F.M.
N	625	6 MHz	4.2 MHz	+4.5 MHz	0.75 MHz	Negative	F.M.

System	Countries
A	United Kingdom, Republic of Ireland.
B	Austria, Australia, West Germany, Italy, Holland, Morocco, New Zealand, Norway, Portugal, Spain, Sweden, Switzerland, Syria, United Arab Republic, Yugoslavia, India, Israel, Malaya, Nigeria etc.
C	Belgium, Luxembourg, Algeria.
D	Czechoslovakia, East Germany, Poland, U.S.S.R.
E	France, Monaco.
F	Luxembourg.
G	Austria, West Germany, Italy, Holland.
H	

I   United Kingdom, Republic of Ireland, South Africa.

J

K

L   France, Luxembourg, Monaco.

M   Canada, Japan, United States of America.

U.K. AND OTHER TELEVISION CHANNEL ASSIGNMENTS

UK BAND I–CHANNEL FREQUENCIES (no longer in use)

	Frequencies	
Channel	Sound	Vision
1	41.50 MHz	45.00 MHz
2	48.25 MHz	51.75 MHz
3	53.25 MHz	56.75 MHz
4	58.25 MHz	61.75 MHz
5	63.25 MHz	66.75 MHz

All transmissions on 405 line system (System A).

UK BAND III–CHANNEL FREQUENCIES

	Frequencies	
Channel	Sound	Vision
6	176.25 MHz	179.75 MHz
7	181.25 MHz	184.75 MHz
8	186.25 MHz	189.75 MHz
9	191.25 MHz	194.75 MHz
10	196.25 MHz	199.75 MHz
11	201.25 MHz	204.75 MHz
12	206.25 MHz	209.75 MHz
13	211.25 MHz	214.75 MHz

All transmissions on 405 line system (System A).

UK BAND IV–CHANNEL FREQUENCIES

Channel	Frequency (MHz)		Channel	Frequency (MHz)	
	Vision	Sound		Vision	Sound
21	471.25 —	477.25	28	527.25 —	533.25
22	479.25 —	485.25	29	535.25 —	541.25
23	487.25 —	493.25	30	543.25 —	549.25
24	495.25 —	501.25	31	551.25 —	557.25
25	503.25 —	509.25	32	559.25 —	565.25
26	511.25 —	517.25	33	567.25 —	573.25
27	519.25 —	525.25	34	575.25 —	581.25

All transmissions on 625 line system (System I).

UK BAND V– CHANNEL FREQUENCIES

Channel	Frequency (MHz) Vision	Sound	Channel	Frequency (MHz) Vision	Sound
39	615.25 —	621.25	54	735.35 —	741.25
40	623.25 —	629.25	55	743.25 —	749.25
41	631.25 —	637.25	56	751.25 —	757.25
42	639.25 —	645.25	57	759.25 —	765.25
43	647.25 —	653.25	58	767.25 —	773.25
44	655.25 —	661.25	59	775.25 —	781.25
45	663.25 —	669.25	60	783.25 —	789.25
46	671.25 —	677.25	61	791.25 —	797.25
47	679.25 —	685.25	62	799.25 —	805.25
48	687.25 —	693.25	63	807.25 —	813.25
49	695.25 —	701.25	64	815.25 —	821.25
50	703.25 —	709.25	65	823.25 —	829.25
51	711.25 —	717.25	66	831.25 —	837.25
52	719.25 —	725.25	67	839.25 —	845.25
53	727.25 —	733.25	68	847.25 —	853.25

All transmissions on 625 line system (System I).

AUSTRALIAN TELEVISION CHANNEL FREQUENCIES

Channel	Frequencies	Channel	Frequencies
0	46.25– 51.75 MHz	6	175.25–180.75 MHz
1	57.25– 62.75 MHz	7	182.25–187.75 MHz
2	64.25– 69.75 MHz	8	189.25–194.75 MHz
3	86.25– 91.75 MHz	9	196.25–201.75 MHz
4	95.25–100.75 MHz	10	209.25–214.75 MHz
5	102.25–107.75 MHz	11	216.25–221.75 MHz
5A	138.25–143.75 MHz		

All transmissions on 625 lines (System B).

NEW ZEALAND TELEVISION CHANNEL FREQUENCIES

Channel	Frequencies	Channel	Frequencies
1	45.25– 50.75 MHz	6	189.25–194.75 MHz
2	55.25– 60.75 MHz	7	196.25–201.75 MHz
3	62.25– 67.75 MHz	8	203.25–208.75 MHz
4	175.25–180.75 MHz	9	210.25–215.75 MHz
5	182.25–187.75 MHz		

All transmissions on 625 lines (System B).

REPUBLIC OF IRELAND TELEVISION CHANNEL FREQUENCIES

Channel	Frequencies	Channel	Frequencies
7*	181.25–184.75 MHz	IE†	183.25–189.25 MHz
11*	201.25–204.75 MHz	IF†	191.25–197.25 MHz
IA†	45.75– 51.75 MHz	IG†	199.25–205.25 MHz
IB†	53.75– 59.75 MHz	IH†	207.25–213.25 MHz
IC†	61.75– 67.75 MHz	IJ†	215.25–221.25 MHz
ID†	175.25–181.25 MHz		

* 425 lines system (System A).   † 625 lines system (System I).

SOUTH AFRICA TELEVISION CHANNEL FREQUENCIES

Channel	Frequencies	Channel	Frequencies
4	175.25–181.25 MHz	9	215.25–221.25 MHz
5	183.25–189.25 MHz	10	223.25–229.25 MHz
6	191.25–197.25 MHz	11	231.25–237.25 MHz
7	199.25–205.25 MHz	13	247.43–253.43 MHz
8	207.25–213.25 MHz		

All transmissions on 625 lines (System I).

U.S. TELEVISION CHANNEL ASSIGNMENTS

V.H.F.

Channel	Frequencies	Channel	Frequencies
2	55.25– 59.75 MHz	8	181.25–185.75 MHz
3	61.25– 65.75 MHz	9	187.25–191.75 MHz
4	67.25– 71.75 MHz	10	193.25–197.75 MHz
5	77.25– 81.75 MHz	11	199.25–203.75 MHz
6	83.25– 87.75 MHz	12	205.25–209.75 MHz
7	175.25–179.75 MHz	13	211.25–215.75 MHz

U.H.F.

Channel	Frequencies	Channel	Frequencies
14	471.25–475.75 MHz	21	513.25–517.75 MHz
15	477.25–481.75 MHz	22	519.25–523.75 MHz
16	483.25–487.75 MHz	23	525.25–529.75 MHz
17	489.25–493.75 MHz	24	531.25–535.75 MHz
18	495.25–499.75 MHz	25	537.25–541.75 MHz
19	501.25–505.75 MHz	26	543.25–547.75 MHz
20	507.25–51i.75 MHz	27	549.25–553.75 MHz

Channel	Frequencies	Channel	Frequencies
28	555.25−559.75 MHz	56	723.25−727.75 MHz
29	561.25−565.75 MHz	57	729.25−733.75 MHz
30	567.25−571.75 MHz	58	735.25−739.75 MHz
31	573.25−577.75 MHz	59	741.25−745.75 MHz
32	579.25−583.75 MHz	60	747.25−751.75 MHz
33	585.25−589.75 MHz	61	753.25−757.75 MHz
34	591.25−595.75 MHz	62	759.25−763.75 MHz
35	597.25−601.71 MHz	63	765.25−769.75 MHz
36	603.25−607.75 MHz	64	771.25−775.75 MHz
37	609.25−613.75 MHz	65	777.25−781.75 MHz
38	615.25−619.75 MHz	66	783.25−787.75 MHz
39	621.25−625.75 MHz	67	789.25−793.75 MHz
40	627.25−631.75 MHz	68	795.25−799.75 MHz
41	633.25−637.75 MHz	69	801.25−805.75 MHz
42	639.25−643.75 MHz	70	807.25−811.75 MHz
43	645.25−649.75 MHz	71	813.25−817.75 MHz
44	651.25−655.75 MHz	72	819.25−823.75 MHz
45	657.25−661.75 MHz	73	825.25−829.75 MHz
46	663.25−667.75 MHz	74	831.25−835.75 MHz
47	669.25−673.75 MHz	75	837.25−841.75 MHz
48	675.25−679.75 MHz	76	843.25−847.75 MHz
49	681.25−685.75 MHz	77	849.25−853.75 MHz
50	687.25−691.75 MHz	78	855.25−859.75 MHz
51	693.25−697.75 MHz	79	861.25−865.75 MHz
52	699.25−703.75 MHz	80	867.25−871.75 MHz
53	705.25−709.75 MHz	81	873.25−877.75 MHz
54	711.25−715.75 MHz	82	879.25−883.75 MHz
55	717.25−721.75 MHz	83	885.25−889.75 MHz

All transmissions on 525 lines (System M).

STANDARD FREQUENCY AND TIME TRANSMISSIONS

Standard frequency transmission (modulated or carrier only) can generally be received on 2500 kHz, 5 MHz, 10 MHz, 15 MHz, 20 MHz and 25 MHz. Some transmissions on these frequencies include time information given by voice announcement, tone pips or BCD (Binary Coded Decimal) time code. Standard time transmission (using BCD) are also made on 60 kHz.

The reception of standard frequency or time transmissions will be dependent on the listener's location, the time of day and time of year. Standard frequency transmissions identify themselves by call sign (usually in voice). Standard time transmissions can usually be identified by their format as given below.

(Some stations announce time in UTC − Universal Co-ordinated Time. For all practical purposes this is the same as GMT − Greenwich Mean Time).

STANDARD TIME TRANSMISSIONS

Station	Location	Frequency	Transmission
VNG	Victoria, Australia	4500 kHz 7.5 MHz 12 MHz	Seconds markers, voice identification
CHU	Ottawa, Canada	3330 kHz 7.335 MHz 14.670 MHz	Seconds markers, voice announcements
BPM	Xian, China	10 MHz 15 MHz	Seconds markers, morse and voice identification
HD210A	Guayaquil, Ecuador	1500 kHz 3.810 MHz 7.6 MHz	Tone pulses, voice announcements
DCF77	Mainflingen Federal Republic of Germany	77.5 kHz	Coded transmission of time and date
ATA	New Delhi, India	5 MHz 10 MHz 15 MHz	Seconds markers, voice identification
JJY	Japan	2500 kHz 5 MHz 8 MHz 10 MHz 15 MHz	Tone pulses, time and identification in morse and voice
ZUO	Olifantsfontein, Republic of South Africa	2500 kHz 5 MHz 100 MHz	Seconds markers, time and identication by morse
HBG	Switzerland	75 kHz	On/off carrier
MSF	Rugby, England	60 kHz 2500 kHz 5 MHz 10 MHz	BCD time, identification by morse
WWV WWVB	Colorado, U.S.A.	60 kHz (WWVB) 2500 kHz (WWV) 5 MHz 10 MHz 15 MHz	BCD time Tone signals and voice announcements (male)
WWVH	Hawaii, U.S.A.	2500 kHz 5 MHz 10 MHz 15 MHz	Tone signals and voice announcement (female)
YVTO	Caracas, Venezuela	6.10 MHz	Seconds markers, voice identification

DESIGNATION OF RADIO EMISSIONS

FIRST SYMBOL

Type of modulation of the main carrier

N   Emission of an unmodulated carrier

Emission in which the main carrier is amplitude-modulated (including cases where sub-carriers are angle-modulated)

A   Double-sideband

H   Single-sideband, full carrier

R   Single-sideband, reduced or variable level carrier

J   Single sideband, suppressed carrier

B   Independent sideband

C   Vestigial sideband

Emission in which the main carrier is angle-modulated

F   Frequency modulation

G   Phase modulation

D   Emission in which the main carrier is amplitude- and angle-modulated either simultaneously or in a pre-established sequence

Emission of pulses

P   Unmodulated sequence of pulses

K   A sequence of pulses modulated in amplitude

L   A sequence of pulses modulated in width/duration

M   A sequence of pulses modulated in position phase

Q   A sequence of pulses in which the carrier is angle-modulated during the period of the pulse.

V   A sequence of pulses which is a combination of the foregoing or is produced by other means.

W   Cases not covered above, in which an emission consists of the main carrier modulated either simultaneously or in a pre-established sequence in a combination of two or more of the following modes: amplitude, angle, pulse.

X   Cases not otherwise covered.

SECOND SYMBOL

Nature of signal(s) modulating the main carrier

0   No modulating signal

1   A single channel containing quantised or digital information without the use of a modulating sub-carrier†

2   A single channel containing quantised or digital information with the use of a modulating sub-carrier†

3   A single channel containing analogue information

7   Two or more channels containing quantised or digital information

8   Two or more channels containing analogue information

9   Composite system with one or more channels containing quantised or digital information, together with one or more channels containing analogue information

X   Cases not otherwise covered

† This excludes time-division multiplex

THIRD SYMBOL

Type of information to be transmitted‡

N No information transmitted
A Telegraph – for aural reception
B Telegraph – for automatic reception
C Facsimile
D Data transmission, telemetry, telecommand
E Telephony (including sound broadcasting)
F Television (video)
W Combination of any of the above
X Cases not otherwise covered

‡ In this context the word 'information' does not include information of a constant, unvarying nature such as provided by standard frequency emissions, continuous wave and pulse radars etc.

EXAMPLE DESIGNATIONS

Old Code*	Emission	Code
A0	CW no modulation	NON
A1	CW keyed carrier	A1A
A2	MCW double sideband keyed tone	A2A
A2A	MCW single sideband reduced carrier	R2A
A2H	MCW single sideband full carrier keyed tone	H2A
A2J	MCW single sideband suppressed carrier keyed tone	J2A
A3	AM double sideband telephony	A3E
A3A	Single sideband reduced carrier telephony	R3E
A3B	Two independent sidebands telephony	B8E
A3H	Compatible AM single sideband plus full carrier telephony	H3E
A3J	Single sideband suppressed carrier telephony	J3E
F1	FSK without use of modulating audio frequency	F1B
F2	FSK with use of modulating audio frequency	F2B
F3	FM telephony	F3E
A7A	Single sideband reduced carrier voice frequency telegraphy	R7A
A9B	Two independent sidebands for combination of telephony and telegraphy	B9W

*pre 1982

EXPRESSION OF BANDWIDTH

A four symbol code uses three numerals to express bandwidth to three significant figures with a letter to denote the unit of frequency placed in the position of the decimal point.

Bandwidths between 0.001 and 999 Hz are expressed in Hz (Letter H)
Bandwidths between 1.00 and 999 kHz are expressed in kHz (Letter K)
Bandwidths between 1.0 and 999 MHz are expressed in MHz (Letter M)
Bandwidths between 1.0 and 999 GHz are expressed in GHz (Letter G)

Examples

0.2 Hz	becomes H200	480 KHz	becomes 480K
35.7 Hz	becomes 35H7	1.4 MHz	becomes 1M40
500 Hz	becomes 500H	24 MHz	becomes 24M0
2.4 kHz	becomes 2K40	321 MHz	becomes 321M
6 kHz	becomes 6K00		

CLASSES OF RADIO STATIONS (AS DEFINED BY ITU)

AL	Aeronautical radionavigation land station
AM	Aeronautical radionavigation mobile station
AT	Amateur station
AX	Aeronautical fixed station
BC	Broadcasting station, sound
BT	Broadcasting station, television
CA	Cargo ship
CO	Station open to official correspondence exclusively
CP	Station open to public correspondence
CR	Station open to limited public correspondence
CV	Station open exclusively to correspondence of a private agency
DR	Directive antenna provided with a reflector
EA	Space station in the amateur-satellite service
EB	Space station in the broadcasting-satellite service (sound broadcasting)
EC	Space station in the fixed-satellite service
ED	Space telecommand space station
EE	Space station in the standard frequency-satellite service
EF	Space station in the radiodetermination-satellite service
EG	Space station in the maritime mobile-satellite service
EH	Space research space station
EJ	Space station in the aeronautical mobile-satellite service
EK	Space tracking space station
EM	Meteorological-satellite space station
EN	Radionavigation-satellite space station
EO	Space station in the aeronautical radionavigation-satellite service
EQ	Space station in the maritime radionavigation-satellite service
ER	Space telemetering space station
ES	Station in the intersatellite service
EU	Space station in the land mobile-satellite service
EV	Space station in the broadcasting-satellite service (television)
EW	Space station in the earth exploration-satellite service
EX	Experimental station
EY	Space station in the time signal-satellite service
FA	Aeronautical station
FB	Base station
FC	Coast station
FL	Land station
FP	Port station
FR	Receiving station only, connected with the general network of telecommunication channels
FS	Land station established solely for the safety of life

FX	Fixed station
GS	Station on board a warship or a military or naval aircraft
LR	Radiolocation land station
MA	Aircraft station
ME	Space station
ML	Land mobile station
MO	Mobile station
MR	Radiolocation mobile station
MS	Ship station
ND	Non-directional antenna
NL	Maritime radionavigation land station
OD	Oceanographic data station
OE	Oceanographic data interrogating station
OT	Station open exclusively to operational traffic of the service concerned
PA	Passenger ship
RA	Radio astronomy station
RC	Non-directional radio beacon
RD	Directional radio beacon
RG	Radio direction-finding station
RM	Maritime radionavigation mobile station
RT	Revolving radio beacon
SM	Meteorological aids station
SS	Standard frequency and time signal station
TA	Space operation earth station in the amateur-satellite service
TB	Fixed earth station in the aeronautical mobile-satellite service
TC	Earth station in the fixed-satellite service
TD	Space telecommand earth station
TE	Transmitting earth station
TF	Fixed earth station in the radiodetermination-satellite service
TG	Mobile earth station in the maritime mobile-satellite service
TH	Earth station in the space research service
TI	Earth station in the maritime mobile-satellite service at a specified fixed point
TJ	Mobile earth station in the aeronautical mobile-satellite service
TK	Space tracking earth station
TL	Mobile earth station in the radiodetermination-satellite service
TM	Earth station in the meteorological-satellite service
TN	Earth station in the radionavigation-satellite service
TO	Mobile earth station in the aeronautical radionavigation-satellite service
TP	Receiving earth station
TQ	Mobile earth station in the maritime radionavigation-satellite service
TR	Space telemetering earth station
TS	Television, sound channel
TT	Earth station in the space operation service
TU	Mobile earth station in the land mobile-satellite service
TV	Television, vision channel
TW	Earth station in the earth exploration-satellite service
TX	Fixed earth station in the maritime radionavigation-satellite service
TY	Fixed earth station in the land mobile-satellite service
TZ	Fixed earth station in the aeronautical radionavigation-satellite service

10 Addresses

ANSI   American National Standards Institute,
1430 Broadway,
NEW YORK,
NY 10018
United States of America

AFDEC   Association of Franchised Distributors of Electronic Components,
Owles Hall,
BUNTINGFORD,
Herts SG9 9PL

AICS   Association of Independent Computer Specialists,
Leicester House,
8 Leicester Street,
LONDON WC2H 7BN

APCC   Association of Professional Computer Consultants,
109 Baker Street,
LONDON W1M 2BH

BCS   British Computer Society,
13 Mansfield Street,
LONDON W1M 0BP

BEAMA   British Electrical & Allied Manufactuers Association,
Leicester House,
8 Leicester Street,
LONDON WC2H 7BN

BSI   British Standards Institution,   *Also*:
2 Park Street,   British Standards Institution,
LONDON W1A 2BS   Linford Wood,
                              MILTON KEYNES MK14 6LE

CCITT   The International Telegraph and Telephone Consultative Committee,
Place des Nations,
CH-1211, GENEVA 20,
Switzerland

CRA   Computer Retailers Association,
           Owles Hall,
           BUNGTINGFORD,
           Herts SG9 9PL

CSA   Computing Services Association,
           Hanover House,
           73 High Holborn,
           LONDON WC1V 6LE

ECMA   European Computer Manufacturers' Association,
           rue du Rhône 114,
           CH-1204, GENEVA,
           Switzerland

ECOMA   European Computer Measurement Association,
           Scheuchzerstrasse 5,
           CH-8006, ZURICH,
           Switzerland

ECSA   European Computing Services Association,
           89 Bierbeekstraat,
           3040 KORBEEK LO,
           Belgium

EEMAC   Electrical & Electronic Manufacturing Association of Canad
           Suite 1608,
           1 Yonge Street,
           TORONTO,
           Ontario M5E 1R1,
           Canada

EIA   Electronic Industries Association,
           2001 Eye Street NW,
           WASHINGTON,
           DC 20006
           United States of America

ERA   Electrical Research Association,
           Cleeve Road,
           LEATHERHEAD,
           Surrey KT22 7SA

IEE   Institution of Electrical Engineers,
           Surrey Place,
           LONDON WC2R 0BL

IEEE Institute of Electrical & Electronic Engineers,
345 E. 47 St,
NEW YORK,
NY 10017,
United States of America

IERE Institution of Electronic & Radio Engineers,
99 Gower Street,
LONDON WC1E 6AZ

IDPM Institute of Data Processing Management,
50 Goschen Buildings,
12 Henrietta Street,
LONDON WC2E 8NU

ISO International Standards Organisation,
1 rue de Varembé,
Case Postale 56,
CH-1211, GENEVA 20,
Switzerland

ITU International Telecommunications Union,
Place des Nations,
CH-1211, GENEVA,
Switzerland

NCC National Computing Centre,
Oxford Road,
MANCHESTER M1 7ED
England

OECD Organisation for Economic Co-operation and Development,
2 rue André-Pascal,
F-75775, PARIS,
France

TUA Telecommunication Users' Association,
Tress House,
3-7 Stamford St,
LONDON SE1

TEMA Telecommunications Engineering & Manufacturers Association,
Leicester House,
8 Leicester Street,
LONDON WC2H 7BN

11 Calculations

OHM'S LAW

For a unidirectional current of constant magnitude flowing in a metallic conductor:

when I = current in amperes
     E = voltage in volts
     R = resistance in ohms
     W = power in watts,

then $I = \dfrac{E}{R} = \dfrac{W}{E} = \dfrac{W}{R}$

$E = IR = \dfrac{W}{I} = WR$

$R = \dfrac{E}{I} = \dfrac{E^2}{W} = \dfrac{W}{I^2}$

$W = EI = I^2R = \dfrac{E^2}{R}$

ELECTRICAL FORMULAE

CAPACITANCE

$$C = \left(\frac{0.0885}{d}\right) KA \text{ picofarads,}$$

where K = dielectric constant
     A = area of plate in sq cm
     d = dielectric thickness in cm

INDUCTANCE

$$\text{(wire) } L = 0.0021 \left(2.303 \log_{10} \frac{4l}{d} - 1\right) \text{ microhenry,}$$

where l = length of straight round wire in cm
     d = diameter of wire in cm

$$\text{(coil) } L = \frac{a^2 N^2}{9a + 10l} \text{ microhenry,}$$

where N = number of turns
a = radius of coil
l = length of coil

IMPEDANCE

$$Z = \sqrt{\left(R^2 + \left(wL - \frac{1}{wC} \right)^2 \right)}$$

where R = resistance in ohms
L = inductance in henrys
C = capacitance in farads
$w = 2\pi f$

CHARACTERISTIC IMPEDANCE

$$(\text{open wire}) \ Z = 276 \log \frac{2D}{d} \text{ ohms,}$$

where D = wire spacing ⎫
d = wire diameter ⎬ in same units
⎭

$$(\text{coaxial}) \ Z = \frac{138}{\sqrt{(K)}} \log \frac{d_o}{d_i} \text{ ohms,}$$

where K = dielectric constant
d_o = outside diameter of inner conductor
d_i = inside diameter of outer conductor

REACTANCE

$$XL = 2\pi fL \text{ ohms}$$

$$XC = \frac{1}{2\pi fC} \text{ ohms,}$$

where f = frequency in hertz
L = inductance in henrys
C = capacitance in farads

RESONANCE (OF TUNED CIRCUIT)

$$f = \frac{1}{2\pi \sqrt{(LC)}} \text{ hertz}$$

$$L = \frac{1}{4\pi^2 f^2 C} \text{ henrys}$$

$$C = \frac{1}{4\pi^2 f^2 L} \text{ farads,}$$

where L = inductance in henrys
C = capacitance in farads
f = frequency in hertz

TIME CONSTANT

$$t = L/R$$
$$t = CR,$$

where t = time in seconds
        L = inductance in henrys
        C = capacitance in farads
        R = resistance in ohms

POWER RATIO

$$P = 10 \log \frac{P_1}{P_2},$$

where P = ratio in decibels
      P_1 and P_2 are the two power levels

DYNAMIC RESISTANCE

$$\text{(of tuned circuit at resonance) } Rd = \frac{L}{Cr} = 2\pi f \, QL = \frac{Q}{2\pi fC},$$

where L = inductance in henrys
        C = capacitance in farads
        f = frequency in hertz
        Q = Q-value of coil

Q (OF INDUCTANCE)

$$Q = \frac{2\pi fL}{R}$$

where f = frequency in hertz
      L = inductance in henrys
      R = series resistance in ohms

COMPONENTS IN SERIES

resistors $R = R1 + R2 + R3 \ldots$
inductors $L = L1 + L2 + L3 \ldots$
capacitor $\dfrac{1}{C} = \dfrac{1}{C1} + \dfrac{1}{C2} + \dfrac{1}{C3} \ldots$

COMPONENTS IN PARALLEL

resistors $\dfrac{1}{R} = \dfrac{1}{R1} + \dfrac{1}{R2} + \dfrac{1}{R3} \ldots$

inductors $\dfrac{1}{L} = \dfrac{1}{L1} + \dfrac{1}{L2} + \dfrac{1}{L3} \ldots$

capacitors $C = C1 + C2 + C3 \ldots$

12 Miscellaneous

WORLD TIME IN ALL COUNTRIES

DIFFERENCE BETWEEN LOCAL TIME AND GREENWICH MEAN TIME

Differences marked + indicate the number of hours ahead of GMT. Differences marked − indicate the number of hours behind GMT.

	Normal Time	Summer Time		Normal Time	Summer Time
Afghanistan	+4½	+4½	Brazil		
Alaska	−8	−7	(a) Oceanic		
	−9	−8	Islands	−2	−2
	−10	−9	(b) Eastern &		
	−11	−10	Coastal	−3	−3
Albania	+1	+2	(c) Manaos	−4	−4
Algeria	GMT	+1	(d) Acre	−5	−5
Andorra	+1	+1	Brunei	+8	+8
Angola	+1	+1	Bulgaria	+2	+3
Anguilla	−4	−4	Burma	+6½	+6½
Antigua	−4	−4	Burundi	+2	+2
Argentina	−3	−3			
Ascension Island	GMT	GMT	Cameroon	+1	+1
Australia			Canada		
(a) Victoria,			(a) Newfoundland	−3½	−2½
New South			(b) Atlantic		
Wales	+10	+11	(Labrador,		
Queensland	+10	+10	Nova Scotia)	−4	−3
Tasmania	+10	+11	(c) Eastern		
(b) Northern			(Ontario)		
Territory	+9½	+9½	Quebec	−5	−4
(c) South			(d) Central		
Australia	+9½	+10½	(Manitoba)	−6	−5
(d) Western			(e) Mountain		
Australia	+8	+8	(Alberta)		
Austria	+1	+2	North West		
Azores	−1	GMT	Territories		
			(Mountain)	−7	−6
Bahamas	−5	−4	(f) Pacific		
Bahrain	+3	+3	(British		
Bangladesh	+6	+6	Columbia)		
Barbados	−4	−4	North West		
Belgium	+1	+2	Territories		
Belize	−6	−6	(West)		
Benin	+1	+1	Yukon	−8	−7
Bermuda	−4	−3	Canary Islands	GMT	+1
Bhutan	+6	+6	Cape Verde Islands	−1	−1
Bolivia	−4	−4	Cayman Islands	−5	−5
Bophuthatswana	+2	+2	Central African		
Botswana	+2	+2	Republic	+1	+1

	Normal Time	Summer Time		Normal Time	Summer Time
Chad	+1	+1	Guam	+10	+10
Chile	−4	−3	Guatemala	−6	−6
China (People's			Guiana (French)	−3	−3
Republic of)	+8	+8	Guinea	GMT	GMT
Christmas Island	+7	+7	Guinea-Bissau	GMT	GMT
Cocos (Keeling)			Guyana		
Islands	+6½	+6½	(Republic of)	−3	−3
Colombia	−5	−5			
Comoro Islands	+3	+3	Haiti	−5	−5
Congo (People's			Hawaii	−10	−10
Republic of)	+1	+1	Honduras		
Cook Islands	−10	−9½	(Republic of)	−6	−6
Costa Rica	−6	−6	Hong Kong	+8	+8
Cuba	−5	−4	Hungary	+1	+2
Cyprus	+2	+3			
Cyprus			Iceland	GMT	GMT
(Turkish Sector)	+3	+3	India	+5½	+5½
Czechoslovakia	+1	+2	Indonesia		
			(a) Java		
Denmark	+1	+2	(Sumatra,		
Diego Garcia	+5	+5	Bali)	+7	+7
Djibouti	+3	+3	(b) Kalimantan		
Dominica	−4	−4	(Sulawesi,		
Dominican Republic	−4	−4	Timor)	+8	+8
			(c) Moluccas,		
Easter Island	−7	−6	West Irian	+9	+9
Ecuador	−5	−5	Iran	+3½	+4½
Egypt	+2	+2	Iraq	+3	+3
El Salvador	−6	−6	Ireland	GMT	+1
Equatorial Guinea	+1	+1	Israel	+2	+2
Ethiopia	+3	+3	Italy	+1	+2
			Ivory Coast	GMT	GMT
Falkland Islands	−4	−4			
(Port Stanley)	−3	−3	Jamaica	−5	−4
Faroe Islands	GMT	+1	Japan	+9	+9
Fiji	+12	+12	Johnston Island	−10	−10
Finland	+2	+3	Jordan	+2	+3
France	+1	+2			
			Kampuchea	+7	+7
Gabon	+1	+1	Kenya	+3	+3
Gambia	GMT	GMT	Kiribati	+12	+12
Germany	+1	+2	Korea, Republic of	+9	+9
Ghana	GMT	GMT	Korea, Democratic		
Gibraltar	+1	+1	Republic of	+9	+9
Greece	+2	+3	Kuwait	+3	+3
Greenland					
Scoresby Sound	−1	GMT	Laos	+7	+7
Angmagssalik,			Lebanon	+2	+3
West Coast			Lesotho	+2	+2
(except Thule)	−3	−2	Liberia	GMT	GMT
Thule area	−4	−4	Libya	+2	+2
Grenada	−4	−4	Lord Howe Island	+10½	+11½
Guadeloupe	−4	−4	Luxembourg	+1	+2

	Normal Time	Summer Time		Normal Time	Summer Time
Macao	+8	+8	Philippines	+8	+8
Madagascar	+3	+3	Poland	+1	+2
Madeira	GMT	GMT	Polynesia (French)	−10	−10
Malawi	+2	+2	Ponape	+11	+11
Malaysia	+7½	+7½	Portugal	GMT	+1
Maldive Islands	+5	+5	Puerto Rico	−4	−4
Mali	GMT	GMT			
Malta	+1	+2	Qatar	+3	+3
Marshall Islands	+12	+12			
Martinique	−4	−4	Reunion	+4	+4
Mauritania	GMT	GMT	Romania	+2	+3
Mauritius	+4	+4	Rwanda	+2	+2
Mayotte (Comoro Islands)	+3	+3	Sabah	+8	+8
Mexico			Saint Helena	GMT	+1
(a) Mexico City	−6	−6	Saint Kitts	−4	−4
(b) Lower California, Pacific			Saint Lucia	−4	−4
Coast	−7	−7	Saint Pierre	−3	−3
(c) Northern part	−8	−7	Saint Vincent	−4	−4
Midway Island	−11	−11	Samoa Islands	−11	−11
Monaco	+1	+2	São Tomé	GMT	GMT
Mongolia	+8	+8	Sarawak	+8	+8
Montserrat	−4	−4	Saudi Arabia	+3	+3
Morocco	GMT	GMT	Senegal	GMT	GMT
Mozambique	+2	+2	Seychelles	+4	+4
			Sierra Leone	GMT	GMT
			Singapore	+7½	+7½
Namibia	+2	+2	Solomon Islands	+11	+11
Nauru	+11½	+11½	Somalia	+3	+3
Nepal	+5hr 40 min	+5hr 40 min	South Africa, Republic of	+2	+2
Netherlands	+1	+2	Spain	+1	+2
Netherlands Antilles	−4	−4	Sri Lanka	+5½	+5½
			Sudan	+2	+2
New Caledonia	+11	+11	Surinam	−3½	−3½
New Zealand	+12	+13	Swaziland	+2	+2
Nicaragua	−6	−6	Sweden	+1	+2
Niger	+1	+1	Switzerland	+1	+2
Nigeria	+1	+1	Syria	+2	+2
Niue	−11	−11			
Norfolk Island	+11½	+11½	Taiwan	+8	+8
Northern Marianas	+10	+10	Tanzania	+3	+3
Norway	+1	+2	Thailand	+7	+7
			Togo	GMT	GMT
Oman	+4	+4	Tonga Islands	+13	+13
			Transkei	+2	+2
Pakistan	+5	+5	Trinidad and Tobago	−4	−4
Palau	+9	+9	Tristan da Cunha	GMT	GMT
Panama	−5	−5	Truk	+10	+10
Papua/New Guinea	+10	+10	Tunisia	+1	+1
Paraguay	−4	−3	Turks and Caicos Islands	−5	−4
Peru	−5	−5			

	Normal Time	Summer Time		Normal Time	Summer Time
Turkey	+3	+3	Sverdlovsk	+5	+6
Tuvalu	+12	+12	Omsk	+6	+7
			Novosibirsk	+7	+8
Uganda	+3	+3	Irxutsk	+8	+9
United Arab			Yakutsk	+9	+10
Emirates	+4	+4	Vladivostok,		
United Kingdom	GMT	+1	Okhotsk	+10	+11
Upper Volta	GMT	GMT	Magadan	+11	+12
Uruguay	−3	−3	Petropavlovsk	+12	+13
U.S.S.R.			Anadyr	+13	+14
Moscow,					
Leningrad	+3	+4	Vanuatu	+11	+11
United States of America			Vatican City	+1	+2
(a) Eastern	−5	−4	Venezuela	−4	−4
(New York, Detroit,			Vietnam	+7	+7
Washington D.C.,			Virgin Islands	−4	−4
Atlanta, Miami)					
(b) Central	−6	−5	Wake Island	+12	+12
(New Orleans, Dallas			Wallis and Futuna		
Kasas, Chicago)			Islands	+12	+12
(c) Mountain	−7	−6	Western Sahara	GMT	GMT
(Denver, Salt Lake					
City, Phoenix)			Yemen,		
(d) Pacific	−8	−7	Arab Republic	+3	+3
(Seattle, Los			Peoples Democratic		
Angeles, San			Republic of,	+3	+3
Francisco)			Yugoslavia	+1	+2
Upper Volta	GMT	GMT			
Uruguay	−3	−3	Zaire,		
USSR			Kinshasa	+1	+2
Moscow,			Lumbumbashi	+2	+2
Leningrad	+3	+4	Zambia	+2	+2
Rostov	+3	+4	Zimbabwe	+2	+2
Volgograd	+4	+5			

THE INTERNATIONAL PHONETIC ALPHABET (ITU DEFINED)

A	Alpha	H	Hotel	O	Oscar	U	Uniform
B	Bravo	I	India	P	Papa	V	Victor
C	Charlie	J	Juliet	Q	Quebec	W	Whiskey
D	Delta	K	Kilo	R	Romeo	X	X-Ray
E	Echo	L	Lima	S	Sierra	Y	Yankee
F	Foxtrot	M	Mike	T	Tango	Z	Zulu
G	Golf	N	November				

MULTI FREQUENCY (MF) SIGNALLING FREQUENCIES FOR PUSH BUTTON TELEPHONES (CCITT DEFINED)

The telephone push buttons are connected to a set of oscillators which apply a pair of tones to the line each time a button is depressed. Each row and each column is allocated a tone. The two tones sent when a button is depressed are those for the row and column in which the button lies.

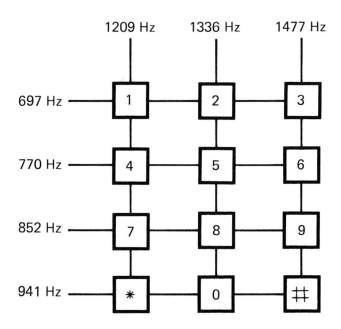

Tones for multi-frequency local signalling

SERVICE CODES AND ABBREVIATIONS USED IN GENTEX AND TELEX OPERATION (AS DEFINED BY ITU)

A	Service telegrams or advices
ABS	Absent subscriber *or* Office closed
ADG	Service telegrams or advices relating to serious interruption of telecommunication routes
ADRS	Address
AMPLIATION	Telegram sent a second time
ANH	Congestion
ANUL	Delete
AURGENT	Service telegrams or advices with urgent transmission and delivery
B	To be used at the beginning of the preamble solely in the exchange of telegrams by Morse and sound—reading instruments and then only when the sending office is working direct with the office of destination

CALL NR	National call number of a GENTEX office
CI	Conversation impossible
CLA	Class of telegram
CR	Confirmation of delivery
CRV	Do you receive well? *or* I receive well
CTA	Communication of all addresses
CTF	Correction to follow
DEB	Overflow position
DER	Out of order
DER BK	Out of order, I cut off
DER MOM	Bad reception, do not cut off, we are testing the line
DETR . . .	I am re-routing to . . . *or* Re-route to . . . *or* Alternative route?
DEVIE	Transmitted by an alternative route
DF	You are in communication with the called subscriber
DTE	Date of handing in
EN CHIFFRES	Telegram, the text of which contains only figures
ETAT	Government telegrams without request for priority
ETATPRIORITE	Government telegrams with request for priority
ETATPRIORITENATIONS	Telegrams relative to the application of the provisions of the United Nations Charter
EXPRES	Express delivery
FS	Reforwarding at the sender's request
FSDEx	Reforwarding at the sender's request from given address(es) (x = name(s) of the office(s) of reforwarding)
FVS	Fives
GP	Poste restante delivery
GPR	Registered poste restante delivery
IND	Answer-back code
INF	Subscriber temporarily unobtainable, call the information service
INQ	Position specializing in the handling of service notes and advices
JFE	Office closed because of holiday
JOUR	Day delivery
Jx	Period of retention of radiotelegrams at land stations (x = number of days)
LR . . .	Acknowledgement of receipt given at the request of the sending operator
LT	Letter telegrams
LTF	Government letter telegrams
LX	De luxe form
LXDEUIL	De luxe form of condolence
MANDAT	Money order telegrams and postal cheque telegrams
MNS	Minutes
MOM	Wait or waiting

MOM PPR	Please wait! I have paper trouble
MP	Personal delivery
MUT	Mutilated
NA	Correspondence with this subscriber is not admitted
NA BK	Correspondence with this telegraph office is not admitted. I cut off
NC	No circuit
NCH	Subscriber's number has been changed
NI	No line identification available
NOT R	Not received
NP	The called party is not or is no longer a subscriber
NR	Indicate your call number *or* My call number is . . .
NUIT	Night delivery
0 (repeated)	(figure 0 repeated): Stop your transmission
OBS	Meteorological telegrams
OCC	Subscriber is engaged (occupied)
O/D	Telegraph office of destination
OMTD	Omitted
O/O	Telegraph office of handing in
P (repeated)	Stop your transmission
PAV	Airmail delivery
PAVR	Registered airmail delivery
PC	Request for confirmation of delivery
PERCEVOIR	Redirection charge to be collected from the addressee
POSTE	Post delivery
POSTXP	Dispatch to destination by express post
PPR	Paper
PR	Registered post delivery
PRESSE	Press telegrams
OGA	May I transmit?
QOK	Do you agree?
RAP	I shall call you back
RCT	Telegrams concerning persons protected in time of war by the Geneva Conventions of 12 August 1949
RECT	Correct please *or* I am correcting *or* Correction?
RECT AB . . .	Correct all before . . .
RECT ALL	Correct the whole telegram
RECT BN . . .	Correct all between . . . and . . .
RECT SRL NR	Correct reference number
RECT TG NR	Correct telegram number
RECT TXT	Correct text
RECT WA . . .	Correct word after . . .
RECT WB . . .	Correct word before . . .
REEXPEDIEx	Redirection at the addressee's request (x = name(s) of the office(s) of redirection)
REMETTREx	Specified date delivery (x = date)
RM	Retransmission of radiotelegrams by one or two mobile stations at the sender's request

ROUTE	Route to . . . *or* I am routing for . . . *or* Route?
RPFR TM . . .	Prepare your reperforator because of telegram with multiple addresses
RPFR TXT	Prepare your reperforator because of long or difficult text *or* because of telegrams having the same text
RPx	Prepaid reply (x = amount in gold francs)
RPT AA . . .	Repeat all after . . .
RPT AB . . .	Repeat all before . . .
RPT ALL	Repeat the whole telegram
RPT BN . . .	Repeat all between . . . and . . .
RPT SRL NR	Repeat reference number given by the transmitting office
RPT TG NR	Repeat telegram number
RPT TXT	Repeat text
RPT WA . . .	Repeat word after . . .
RPT WB . . .	Repeat word before . . .
RSBA	Retransmission still being attempted
RST	Reply to paid service advices
SRL NR	Reference number given by a GENTEX transmitting office
SSSS	Change of alphabet
ST	Paid service advices
SVH	Telegrams relating to the safety of life
SVIN	Service indication
TAX	What is the charge *or* The charge is . . .
TAXE PERCUE	Redirection charge collected
TC	Collation (complete repetition at the request of the sender)
TCHN	Technical service *or* I shall advise the technical service
TELEX	Subscriber's telegraph service enabling users to communicate directly and temporarily with one another by means of start-stop apparatus
TEST MSG	Please send a test message
TFx	Telephone delivery (x = telephone number)
TG	Telegram
TG NR . . .	Telegram number given by the handing-in office . . .
THRU	You are in communication with a telex position
TLXx	Telex delivery (x = telex number)
TMx	Multiple addresses (x = number of addresses)
TNS	Tens
TPLE	Triple word(s)
TPR	Teleprinter
TR	Telegraph restante delivery
URGENT	Urgent transmission and delivery
UTCOD	Use the GENTEX code
VIA	Route to be followed
W	Word(s)
WRU	Who is there? *or* Who are you?
XP	Paid express delivery

XQ	Service notes
XXXXX	Error
+?	I have finished my transmission. Do you wish to transmit?

MISCELLANEOUS ABBREVIATIONS AND SIGNALS (AS DEFINED BY ITU)

AA	All after . . .
AB	All before . . .
ABT	About
ADS	Address
AF	Audio frequency
AGN	Again
AM	Amplitude modulation
ANS	Answer
ANT	Antenna
AR	End of transmission (morse code)
AS	Waiting period (morse code)
BC	Broadcast
BD	Bad
BK	Signal used to interrupt a transmission in progress
BN	All between . . . and . . .
BQ	A reply to an RQ
BT	Signal to mark the separation between different parts of the same transmission (morse code)
BTR	Better
C	Yes
CCT	Circuit
CFM	Confirm *or* I confirm
CH	Channel
CK	Check
CL	I am closing my station
CLG	Calling
CLR	Clear
COL	Collate *or* I collate
COR	Correction
CP	General call to two or more specified stations
CQ	General call to all stations
CS	Call sign
CW	Continuous wave
DBL	Double
DCT	Direct
DDD	Used to identify the transmission of the distress message by a station not itself in distress
DE	From
DF	Your bearing at . . . hours was . . . degrees, with a possible error of . . . degrees
DIF	Different
DLD	Delivered
DO	Bearing doubtful. Ask for another bearing later *or* at . . . hours
DR	Dear
DSB	Double sideband
DTG	Date-time group
DUPE	This is a duplicate message
E	East
E E E	Error signal
EHF	Extreme high frequency
EL	Element
ER	Here . . .
ERP	Effective radiated power
ES	And
ETA	Estimated time of arrival
EX	Formerly
FAX	Facsimile
FIG	Figure(s)
FLD	Field
FM	Frequency modulation
FM	From
FSK	Frequency-shift keying
FYI	For your information
GA	You may transmit (Go ahead)
GD	Good
GMT	Greenwich Mean Time
GP	Group
HDG	Heading
HF	High frequency
HI	Laughter
HQ	Headquarters
HR	Hour
HRS	Hours

HW	How	OK	We agree *or* It is correct
ID	Identification	OL	Ocean letter
IMI	Interrogation sign − ? (morse code)	OM	Old man
		OP	Operator
INF	Information	P	Prefix indicating a private radiotelegram
INT	Interrogation sign		
IRPT	I repeat	PBL	Preamble
ISB	Independent sideband	PEP	Peak envelope power
ITP	The punctuation counts	PLS	Please
K	Invitation to transmit	PM	Pulse modulation
KA	Starting signal (morse code)	POS	Position
KC	Kilocycles	PSE	Please
KMH	Kilometres per hour	PT	Part
KTS	Nautical miles per hour (knots)	PTP	Point-to-point
		R	Received
LF	Low frequency	RE	Concerning
LL	Landline	REF	Reference to . . . *or* Refer to . . .
LR	The last message received by me was . . .		
		RF	Radio frequency
LS	The last message sent by me was . . .	RPFR	Reperforator
		RPT	Repeat *or* I repeat *or* Repeat . . .
LSB	Lower sideband		
LTR	Letter(s)	RQ	Indication of a request
LW	Long wave	RTTY	Radioteletype
MAR	Maritime	S	South
MC	Megacycles	SHF	Super high frequency
MC	Multiple copy	SIG	Signature
MF	Medium frequency	SLT	Radiomaritime letter
MIL	Military	SOS	Distress signal (morse code)
MIN	Minute *or* Minutes	SP	Space
MIS	Missing	SRI	Sorry
MK	Mark	SS	Indicator preceding the name of a ship station
MOD	Modulation		
MPH	Statute miles per hour	SSB	Single sideband
MSG	Message	SVC	Prefix indicating a service telegram
MSR	Misrouted		
MUX	Multiplex	SW	Short wave
MW	Medium wave	SYS	Refer to your service telegram
MX	Music	TBL	Trouble
N	North	TFC	Traffic
NBFM	Narrow-band frequency modulation	TMW	Tomorrow
		TR	Used by a land station to request the position and next port of call of a mobile station; used also as a prefix to the reply
ND	Non-directional		
NIL	I have nothing to send to you		
NO	No		
NR	Near		
NR	Number		
NW	Now	TS	Time signal
NX	News *or* Notices	TTT	This group, when sent three times, constitutes the
OBS	Observations		

	safety signal	WB	Word before . . .
TTY	Teletype	WD	Word(s) *or* Group(s)
TU	Thank you	WPM	Words per minute
TV	Television	WTG	Waiting
TX	Transmitter	WX	Weather
TXT	Text	XQ	Prefix used to indicate an operating communication in the fixed service
UHF	Ultra high frequency		
UR	Your		
USB	Upper sideband	XXX	This group, when sent three times, constitutes the urgency signal
UT	Universal Time		
UTC	Coordinated Universal Time		
VA	End of work (morse code)		
VFT	Voice-frequency telegraphy	YES	Yes
VLF	Very low frequency	YR	Year
VVV . . . VVV	Marking *or* Test transmission	YR	Your
		YZ	The words which follow are in plain language
VY	Very	Z	Coordinated Universal Time
W	West	73	Best Wishes
WA	Word after . . .		

TELEPHONE SIGNALLING SYSTEMS

CCITT NO. 1 (OBSOLETE)

For manual use on international circuits. Uses 500 Hz interrupted at 20 Hz for 2 seconds.

CCITT NO. 2 (OBSOLETE)

A 2 VF (two voice frequency) system using 600 Hz and 750 Hz for line supervision and dialling pulses respectively.

CCITT NO. 3 (OBSOLETE)

A 1 VF system using 2280 Hz for line supervision and inter-register signalling. Used for manual and automatic operation with a start-stop code at 20 baud.

CCITT NO. 4

A 2 VF system used only in Europe for manual and automatic signalling on unidirectional international circuits. Line supervision pulses at 2040 Hz and 2400 Hz are 100 m, 150 m or 350 m long. A four element code at 28 baud is used at 2400 Hz for inter-register signalling.

CCITT NO. 5

A 2 VF system using 2400 Hz and 2600 Hz for supervisory signals and 6 inband frequencies for inter-register signalling.

CCITT NO. 5 bis (OBSOLETE)

Used only on French-made equipment and similar to CCITT No. 5 but is 'compelled'.

A 'compelled' signalling system transmits line and supervisory signals continuously until acknowledged by the distant end.

CCITT NO. 6

A common channel system in which signalling information travels over a single common channel serving a number of speech circuits.

Transmissions are digital in nature at 2K4 bps in an analogue system and 4K bps or 56K bps in a digital environment. The basic signalling unit is 28 bits in length.

CCITT NO. 7

A common channel system for use between Stored Programme Control (SPC) exchanges operating at 64K bps. The signalling information occupies up to 279 octets, each of 8 bits in length.

CCITT R1

A 1 VF supervisory system using 2600 Hz with inter-register signalling as CCITT No. 5.

CCITT R2

Line signalling is 1 VF at 3825 Hz (out of band) or, for in-band use, 2 VF using 2040 Hz and 2400 Hz (as CCITT No. 4).

Inter-register signalling is compelled 2 VF in each direction: 1380 Hz and 1980 Hz in the forward direction and 540 Hz and 1140 Hz in the backward direction.

CCITT G732

Used with 30 channel PCM systems operating at 2.048 Mbps. Bit stealing is used to provide 2K bps for voice channel or a single 64K bps common channel.

DC SIGNALLING

Originally the breaking/making of a battery or ground connection from a dial pulse (60% break, 40% make). Now used to signify any signalling system using simple on-off indicators of battery, ground or tone.

CB or Central Battery is a simple contact closure type of DC signalling.

E & M (Ear and Mouth or Earth and Mark) transmits simple on-off signalling on separate signalling circuits. Transmit information is on the M leg and is received on the E leg.

CCIS

Common Channel Inter-Office Signalling is widely used in North America for the exchange of information between SPC systems. Messages are usually passed at 2400 bps over separate common channels. Since signalling is separate from voice a continuity check is made on the voice circuit just prior to switching, using 2010 Hz and 1780 Hz tones.

It is planned to replace CCIS with a system based on CCITT No. 7.

PUBLIC SWITCHED TELEPHONE NETWORK STANDARD TONES (U.K.)

Number unobtainable tone	400 Hz continuously	
Engaged tone	400 Hz interrupted	0.75 seconds On 0.75 seconds Off etc.
or	400 Hz interrupted	0.375 seconds On 0.375 seconds Off etc.
Pay tone	400 Hz interrupted	0.125 seconds On 0.125 seconds Off etc.
Ringing tone	400 Hz *or* 400+450 Hz modulated by 50,25 *or* 17 Hz and interrupted	0.4 seconds On 0.2 seconds Off 0.4 seconds On 2.0 seconds Off etc.
Equipment engaged tone	400 Hz interrupted	0.4 seconds On 0.35 seconds Off 0.225 seconds On 0.525 seconds Off
Timing tones	900 Hz	three periods of 0.15 separated by 0.85 seconds every 3 minutes
Dial tone	50 or 33.3 Hz	

PUBLIC SWITCHED TELEPHONE NETWORK STANDARD TONES (U.S.A.)

Number unobtainable	500 Hz +600 Hz	interrupted once per second
Engaged tone number busy	480 Hz +620 Hz	interrupted once per second

trunk busy	480 Hz +620 Hz	interrupted twice per second
Ringing tone	440 Hz +480 Hz	
Dial tone	350 Hz +440 Hz	
Recorder warning tone	1400 Hz	at 15 second intervals

GREEK ALPHABET

Capital letters	Small letters	Greek name	English equivalent	Capital letters	Small letters	Greek name	English equivalent
A	α	Alpha	a	N	ν	Nu	n
B	β	Beta	b	Ξ	ξ	Xi	x
Γ	γ	Gamma	g	O	o	Omicron	o
Δ	δ	Delta	d	Π	π	Pi	p
E	ϵ	Epsilon	e	P	ρ	Rho	r
Z	ζ	Zeta	z	Σ	σ	Sigma	s
H	η	Eta	é	T	τ	Tau	t
Θ	θ	Theta	th	Υ	υ	Upsilon	u
I	ι	Iota	i	Φ	ϕ	Phi	ph
K	κ	Kappa	k	X	χ	Chi	ch
Λ	λ	Lambda	l	Ψ	ψ	Psi	ps
M	μ	Mu	m	Ω	ω	Omega	ō

Index